Vegetarian Meals

for Babies and Young Children

Vegetarian Meals

for Babies and Young Children

including a comprehensive guide to INTRODUCING SOLIDS

Endorsed by Sydney Adventist Hospital

Natalee McLean

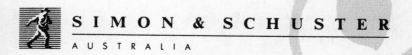

SIMON & SCHUSTER
AUSTRALIA

For

Martine

Jack Bertie

and

Molly

VEGETARIAN MEALS FOR BABIES AND YOUNG CHILDREN

First published in Australia in 1999 by
Simon & Schuster (Australia) Pty Limited
20 Barcoo Street, East Roseville NSW 2069

A Viacom Company
Sydney New York London Toronto Tokyo Singapore

National Library of Australia
Cataloguing-in-Publication data

McLean, Natalee

    Vegetarian meals for babies and young children.

    ISBN 0 7318 0832 0.

    1. Cookery (Baby foods). 2. Vegetarian cookery. I. Title.

641.5622

Design: Green Words & Images, Canberra
Cover illustration: Katie Jordan

Set in Perpetua 12.5/14.5 pt

Printed in Australia by Australian Print Group

10 9 8 7 6 5 4 3 2 1

Acknowledgements

I would first like to thank and praise the Lord God Almighty for blessing me with the experience and wisdom with which to write this book.

A big thank you to my husband Paul for trying all my recipes and giving me lots of encouragement and support.

Thank you to my first writing teacher June Duncan Owen.

Thank you to Karen Guy and Angela Saunders, dietitians at Sydney Adventist Hospital.

I wish to thank the following children for trying my recipes and a big thank you to their mums as well for allowing me to use their children as guinea pigs!

Trent Chandler and his mum Bronwyn

Courtney Tyler and her mum Karen

Rachel Greenland and her mum Ruth

Tijana and Jaevin Lillioja and their mum Sue.

Grateful thanks to Dr James Wright for his wonderful foreword, and to Sydney Adventist Hospital for endorsing this book.

I would also like to thank the team at Simon & Schuster, especially Julie Stanton and Brigitta Doyle, for making it all happen.

And lastly a big thank you to my family and friends for just being there.

Foreword

What a pleasure to read Natalee McLean's new book *Vegetarian Meals for Babies and Young Children*, written especially for bubs and infants. And, more importantly, written for their parents, and that includes grandparents too — for they often have considerable influence on 'bringing up bub'. Deja-vu?

I've now been reviewing new publications for my nationally syndicated newspaper columns and radio programs for more than 30 years. Hundreds, probably thousands, of new volumes have drifted across my desk, and I've perused most at close quarters.

I am delighted to say this must be one of the best in its class. It is sensibly and clearly written, which makes it user-friendly. That in itself is an achievement.

I particularly like the fact it's vegetarian. People following this line of nutrition were once considered cranks, but no longer. It is now an important part of mainstream nutrition, as medical journals regularly testify — and yes, it can be followed right from the start of life.

My old mum, who lived to 100, invariably enjoyed excellent health. She was a life-long vegetarian and so was Dad, who lived for 86 healthy years. Mum's mother likewise followed the vegetarian principle. My two brothers and myself have followed it for a lifetime, and so have my four children, and now nine grandchildren!

The point I am making is that vegetarian living over four generations has been a sheer delight. Simplicity, good health, plenty of stamina and mental acuity have been the major benefits.

I do it for commonsense lifestyle reasons, not for any philosophical ones, although I dislike killing animals for commercial purposes. But I believe that the readily available, high-quality spread of foods in the form of grains, wholemeal bread, cereals, vegetables, fruit, legumes (e.g. peas, beans and lentils), seeds, nuts, soy and dairy products form the basis for good health.

Mum always encouraged modest sweetening (ideally honey or golden syrup in her day), minimum fat and frying, fresh food if possible, and homegrown food whenever available. Dad was an enthusiastic gardener. I kept fowls, there was a cow, and the combined manure fertilised the veggie gardens, fruit trees and flower pots. All organic, non-chemical, excellent forms of fertilisation, even though it did smell a bit!

There is no doubt that sensible eating plans help create good health. Teamed with adequate exercise (even a 30-minute walk a day is fine), fresh air, sufficient rest and a positive outlook on life, they give a good basic start for longevity, and happiness is assured.

This excellent book sets out the basics of sensible baby care. The relatively simple message is clearly sent out. Then, to make it all easier, there are straightforward recipes, incorporating the basics of vegetarian eating.

I am happy to endorse this book, and will certainly be pleased to recommend it to the group of people — usually happy young mums and grans — for whom it is written.

Natalee McLean has drawn on her many years of practical experience and now passes it on to a wider audience. I am sure you will appreciate the time and effort, for it is an enormous undertaking to write a book. To write a successful one, which I believe this is destined to be, is an even greater achievement.

I hope it will find a place in every Australian kitchen, including yours. That's where the meals are prepared!

DR JAMES WRIGHT

SYDNEY 1999

Note from the author

All of the ingredients I've used in the following recipes can be bought at your supermarket or health food shop.

When I refer to the ingredient 'spring onion' I'm referring to the long thin variety, not the one with a large white bulb on the end.

When I refer to 'desired consistency' in the recipes I mean make it to your baby or child's needs. Whether they prefer it thick or thin, pureed or lumpy. You will soon know what your baby or child likes and can cope with. But at the same time it is important to keep challenging them with different textures of food.

Contents

Introduction

Being a vegetarian is a great way to help protect your health. It is known that vegetarians have lower rates of cancer, heart disease, diabetes, obesity, hypertension, gall stones and kidney stones. Vegetarians on the whole eat less fat and cholesterol, eat more fibre and consume more antioxidants.

Vegetarians usually fall into two categories, lacto-ovo and vegan. Lacto-ovo vegetarians still consume dairy products but vegans eat only plant food, including grains, legumes, vegetables, fruits, nuts and seeds. Another category is semi-vegetarians, they eat the same as lacto-ovo vegetarians but still eat small amounts of meat several times a week.

Being a vegetarian myself and enjoying the healthy benefits it brings, as well as the interest and enjoyment of cooking vegetarian meals, prompted me to find out what was available in the way of cookbooks pertaining to babies and children. Over the years I'd come into contact with parents asking for advice and books on this matter. After some research I found that there was not a lot written on this subject. So, after much thought, I decided I would put my mothercraft experience and my interest in vegetarianism together and put pen to paper.

I wanted to write this book not only for vegetarians but also to provide information for parents who wish to supplement their child's meat diet with some vegetarian alternatives, but don't quite know how to go about it.

Introducing solids is an important milestone for you and your baby but sometimes parents are unsure about how to achieve this, so I wanted to provide some simple, straightforward advice.

During my working years as a mothercraft nurse I've always had a passion for education. I'm hoping this passion has come across in this book and that you find the information helpful and useful as well as reassuring.

Nutritional Requirements

There may be a variety of reasons why parents choose a vegetarian diet for their baby or child. It may be because of ethical or religious beliefs or because of views on healthy eating. For whatever reason, the decision to feed your baby or child vegetarian food is becoming more socially and nutritionally acceptable. Today, vegetarian food is exciting; it offers a wonderful array of tastes, colours, textures and appetising smells.

For babies and children, vegetarian food can be nutritionally balanced and cater for their growing needs if meals are planned carefully, keeping the following nutritional requirements in mind. Education is the key!

VARIETY

Try to provide variety in your child's diet, offering as many different kinds of foods as possible. Examples are below, and refer to the Vegetarian Food Pyramid on page 5.

- **Grains**: rice, corn, oats, wheat and its by-products, for example, couscous.

- **Pulses and legumes**: lentils, beans, peas. (If your baby or child is on a full vegetarian diet, try to provide one serving of these a day.)

- **Nuts and seeds**: these come in many forms. Butters and spreads are suitable for older babies and children, for example, tahini (pureed sesame seeds), peanut, cashew, almond and macadamia butters. (If your baby or child is on a full vegetarian diet, try to provide one serving of these a day.) Note: do not offer nut butters and spreads to babies under 12 months. Tahini can be offered instead.

- **Breads, pasta and breakfast cereals**: brown and wholegrain breads are the healthier choice. Choose healthy breakfast cereals. For young babies, use iron-fortified rice cereal and later use products such as Weetbix, which are iron fortified. Porridge, which consists of rolled oats, is also high in iron.

- **Fruit and vegetables**.

- **Dairy**: milk, yoghurt and cheese.

- **Eggs**.

- **Soy products**: tofu, soy milk, soy yogurt and soy cheese.

Iron

Iron is an important nutrient needed by the body to form haemoglobin in the red blood cells, which carries oxygen throughout the body. Iron is also involved in the production of energy, which is important for babies and children. Your baby is born with enough iron for their development but this starts to deplete at around 6 months, so it's important to start including foods in your baby's diet that have a good iron content.

The iron found in plant foods is not as easily absorbed as iron found in animal foods. This is not a problem if in the same meal you provide foods that have a good vitamin C content to help increase the iron absorption. Examples of vitamin C enriched foods that can be combined with iron rich foods are: avocado, banana, carrot, corn, cucumber, eggplant, capsicum, tomato, zucchini, pumpkin, grapes, kiwifruit, citrus fruits, berries, melon, peaches and nectarines. Broccoli, spinach and other green, leafy vegetables are high both in iron and vitamin C. The

Vegetarian Food Pyramid

Use the Vegetarian Food Pyramid as a guide when planning your child's vegetarian meals, as this will help give them a healthy, well-balanced diet.

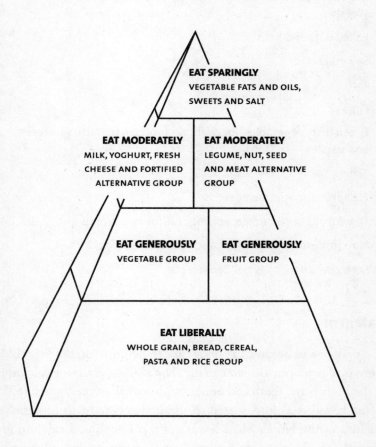

EAT SPARINGLY
VEGETABLE FATS AND OILS, SWEETS AND SALT

EAT MODERATELY
MILK, YOGHURT, FRESH CHEESE AND FORTIFIED ALTERNATIVE GROUP

EAT MODERATELY
LEGUME, NUT, SEED AND MEAT ALTERNATIVE GROUP

EAT GENEROUSLY
VEGETABLE GROUP

EAT GENEROUSLY
FRUIT GROUP

EAT LIBERALLY
WHOLE GRAIN, BREAD, CEREAL, PASTA AND RICE GROUP

Reproduced with slight adaptations with the permission of The Health Connection

choice is wide, so combining vitamin C and iron is not that difficult. Foods that contain iron include:

- Beans, lentils and peas
- Wholegrain bread
- Iron-fortified breakfast cereals, for example, rice cereal and Weetbix
- Rolled oats and bran
- Soy milk
- Tofu
- Eggs
- Green leafy vegetables, for example, broccoli, spinach, silverbeet and parsley
- Tahini
- Pumpkin and sunflower seeds
- Dried fruits, for example, apricots, raisins and prunes
- Nuts, for example, almonds and cashews

NOTE: cow's milk does not contain iron.

Calcium

The denser and heavier the bones are to begin with, the less risk there is of osteoporosis later in life. The storage place for calcium in the body is the teeth and bones, with a small percentage found in the blood. Calcium stored in the bones is used to replenish calcium in the blood when levels get too low. Blood calcium is needed for muscle contraction, nerve transmission and blood clotting. Calcium is well provided during the first 6 months while your baby is breast- or formula-fed. But once weaning begins you need to supplement their diet.

Foods that contain calcium include:

- Cow's milk—not to be offered as a drink to babies under 12 months
- Fortified soy milk—not to be offered as a drink to babies under 12 months
- Plain yoghurt
- Fortified soy yogurt
- Tahini
- Cheese
- Almonds, brazil nuts
- Figs
- Grains
- Beans and lentils
- Dark green leafy vegetables

Vitamin B12

Vitamin B12 is essential for a healthy nervous system and the formation of red blood cells. It is stored in the liver and muscle, and we only need a tiny amount of it; one teaspoon of vitamin B12 is enough to meet the needs of nearly 100 people for their entire lives (Messina and Messina, 1996). But this tiny amount is still very important and we need to know we and our children are getting enough.

Vitamin B12 is found in eggs, and dairy products. So, for a child on an ovo-lacto vegetarian diet getting enough vitamin B12 is not usually a problem. But for a child on a vegan diet it is a different matter, as vitamin B12 is virtually not found in plant foods at all unless they are contaminated by the bacteria that vitamin B12 comes from. Various foods such as soy milk are now being fortified with vitamin B12. Check the labels and consult your doctor or dietitian about whether your child is receiving an adequate amount, as they may need to take a supplement.

Mothers who are vegan and are breastfeeding should be taking a vitamin B12 supplement or food fortified with vitamin B12. It is thought that the mother's stores of the vitamin are not available to the baby through breast milk—only the vitamin B12 she is consuming in her diet at the time are.

Zinc

Zinc is important for growth, wound healing and storage of insulin in the pancreas.

If you are providing a diet for your baby or child that is iron- and calcium-enriched, you will be providing food that has good sources of zinc for growth.

Protein

Contrary to popular belief, we don't need as much protein as was earlier thought. If you are providing wide variety in your child's diet, getting enough protein is not a problem.

Foods that contain protein include:

- Dairy products
- Beans, lentils and peas
- Soy milk
- Tofu
- Eggs
- Nut spreads
- Grains (wheat, oats, corn and rice)
- Seeds
- Bread

- Vegetables
- Meat substitutes, for example, nutmeats

This list of nutrients may be a bit overwhelming at first but, if you refer to this information regularly when planning and cooking your child's meals, providing a nutritionally balanced diet will become second nature to you.

If you have any concerns or questions or if you want more advice about providing a vegetarian diet for your baby or child, please talk to your doctor, paediatrician or dietitian. Also, if your child has any special needs or a medical condition, you will need to consult the doctor, paediatrician or dietitian before commencing a full vegetarian diet.

Energy

It is important to provide your baby or child with high energy foods, as they need this for growth. Being high in fibre, the vegetarian diet can be very bulky. Since children's stomachs are small they can fill up very quickly and miss out on high-calorie food. Morning and afternoon teas, which you can start around 7–8 months, are a good time to provide high-energy foods.

High-energy foods include:

- Fruit
- Avocado
- Cheese
- Nut butters
- Fruit juices

See page 71 for more ideas on morning and afternoon teas.

Milk - the first 12 months

Milk, whether it's breast milk or formula, is the most important food in your baby's first 12 months of life. Breast milk has many benefits.

- Breast milk contains all the nutrients your baby needs, especially for the first 6 months of life.

- The colostrum your baby receives from breast milk in the first few days contains antibodies which help increase your baby's immunity.

- It has been suggested that breast milk lowers the risk of Sudden Infant Death Syndrome.

- Breastfed babies rarely get constipated.

- Breast milk is convenient and cheap—no warming or sterilising required!

For some mothers, breastfeeding is not an option, so infant formula is the next best thing. With up-to-date knowledge and technology, the formula companies are striving to get the formula as close to the real thing as possible.

Cow's milk should not be offered as a drink in a bottle or cup before your baby is 12 months of age. Cow's milk is made for baby calves not for human babies, so it's not nutritionally balanced for your baby's first 12 months of life. It's nutritionally balanced for a cow! Also, the level of protein in cow's milk is too high for a baby to digest. In some babies intestinal bleeding could occur.

After 6 months you can cook with cow's milk to make your baby's meals because the cooking process breaks down the level of protein. At around 8–9 months you can start to use a little cow's milk on your baby's breakfast cereal.

Soy milks also should not be offered as a drink in a bottle or cup to a baby under 12 months of age. There are soy formulas available that are nutritionally balanced for your baby. Again, you can cook with soy milk after 6 months and start to add it to cereal at around 8–9 months.

Rice cereal should never be given in a bottle to your baby. Juice should not be offered until your baby is 6 months of age unless you are giving prune juice for constipation. Small amounts of cooled boiled water in a bottle can be given between feeds if you feel your baby needs some extra fluids in the hot weather or if they are constipated.

When your baby reaches 12 months of age they can start to have cow/soy milk in a bottle or cup to drink to replace the formula. Cow's milk must be full strength, not low fat/light/skinny varieties.

If at 12 months you are still breastfeeding your baby and plan to for a little longer, you could offer some cow's or soy milk in a cup at morning or afternoon tea time or with lunch. Cow's milk contains calcium, protein, zinc and vitamin B12 but no iron. Soy milk is an excellent source of iron and some brands, for example 'So Good', are fortified with calcium and vitamin B12.

All about solids

INTRODUCING SOLIDS

The introduction of solids to your baby's diet is an important event for you and your baby. As your baby grows and develops, solids become an important nutritional addition to the milk diet. Also, introducing solids is an education, as your baby needs to learn to eat, as well as learning to eat a wide variety of foods that come in many sizes, shapes, textures, tastes, colours and smells so they can graduate and enter the adult world of food.

The normal age to commence solids is **4 months**, though breastfed babies sometimes are not ready or interested until 5–6 months. Unless recommended by your doctor for medical reasons, it's not a good idea to offer solids before 4 months as it may put unnecessary strain on their immature digestive system. Also, it's not until 4 months that your baby's tongue thrust/extrusion reflex starts to disappear so offering solids before this time will be difficult and messy.

When commencing solids, the first thing you have to think of is somewhere for your baby to sit. Feeding your baby sitting on your lap can be awkward and they are still too little to sit in a high-chair. A bouncinette/rocker-type seat is an excellent solution.

As for feeding bowls, any small bowl will do. It's not until your baby starts to feed themselves that you will need to invest in a proper feeding bowl. A bowl with a suction rim on the bottom is a great idea as it stays put.

When it comes to feeding spoons, choose a design that best suits you, making sure it's plastic with no hard edges. Do not use a metal spoon at this age as it may damage the soft tissue around your baby's mouth. You don't need to sterilise the bowl and spoon. Make sure both are washed well in warm soapy water, dried and stored in a clean dry spot.

The final thing to remember is to have plenty of bibs and washers on hand as things can get very messy!

The next part of the chapter is written for a baby starting on solids at **4 months**. If you choose to start solids later, follow this progression. The commencement of solids at 4 months does not replace a milk feed but is an addition to the milk diet. Remember that milk (breast or formula) is important for the first 12 months of life. When you are commencing solids at 4 months you do so *after* the milk feed, not before, as milk takes preference. Allow 15–20 minutes after the milk feed before you give the solids. This will allow the milk feed to settle so your baby doesn't feel too full and refuse the solids.

Start with some commercially available rice cereal. When it's made up, rice cereal should have a slightly thicker consistency than milk which is familiar to your baby so they are more likely to take it. The rice cereal is also iron fortified, easily digested and, being made from rice, is less allergenic than other cereals (e.g. wheat).

To prepare rice cereal, add a teaspoon of dry cereal to 1–2 tablespoons of expressed breast milk/formula or cooled boiled water and mix until its consistency is a little thicker than that of milk. Heat only to lukewarm before giving to your baby.

Put the spoon to your baby's mouth to encourage them to open. Once the mouth is open, gently insert the spoon. Your baby may try to lick or suck the cereal off the spoon or push it out with their tongue. If they push it away, try again. If they get distressed, stop and try again later or the next day. Up until now your baby's only eating mechanism has been sucking so, when introducing solids, your baby has to learn to take food from a spoon, masticate and then swallow the solid mass. All this is a new experience and may take from a couple of days to a couple of weeks to master, so don't despair or give up too quickly if your baby is rejecting the solids.

It's normal for a baby first taking solids to gag as they are learning to swallow. If this happens, don't panic or overreact. Just calmly pat your baby firmly on the back between the shoulder blades. It's amazing how quickly a baby picks up on an over-reaction and starts turning it into a game. This can lead to very frustrating and stressful mealtimes. Keep mealtimes as fuss free as possible. If you, or your baby, are getting stressed during the meal, stop and try again later or the next day. Don't force-feed your baby as this can lead to problems down the track.

During the first week of feeding solids, offer some rice cereal once a day. A good time is after the mid-morning or mid-afternoon feed. If your baby is doing well and appears to be enjoying it, increase the amount of rice cereal by 1–2 teaspoons and thicken the consistency by using less milk. During the second week, offer the rice cereal twice a day.

At the beginning of the third week, you can add some pureed fruit to the rice cereal. Start off with some pear or apple as these fruits are fairly alkaline so are gentle on the digestive system. Start with a teaspoon and work up to a large tablespoon of fruit. See recipes for how to prepare fruit. Offer one type of fruit for several days to allow your baby's digestive system to adjust and watch for any allergies. If your baby tolerates fruit, you can introduce a pureed vegetable during the fourth week. Usually pumpkin or sweet potato is good to start with. The table on the following page is a guide to the first 4 weeks of solids.

4 months	week 1	Rice cereal once a day
	week 2	Rice cereal twice a day—morning and afternoon
	week 3	Rice cereal and fruit in morning / Rice cereal in afternoon
	week 4	Rice cereal and fruit in morning / Vegetable in afternoon

Continue the week 4 program for four weeks. During this time you can try pureed fruits such as bananas, apricots, peaches and avocados, and vegies such as zucchini, squash, parsnip, potato and broccoli.

At **5 months** your baby's food routine may look something like this:

5 months	6 am	Milk feed
Times are guidelines only >	10 am	Milk feed / Rice cereal and fruit
	2 pm	Milk feed
	6 pm	Milk feed / Vegies—approx ½ cup
	10 pm	Milk feed

By 5 months your baby should be on five milk feeds a day.

At **6 months** your baby can graduate to a highchair. You may need to use an insert at first to help with the transition, to give your baby a bit more stability and support. Also remember to strap them in to prevent them from slipping, wriggling and climbing out of the chair. It's a long way down for a little person!

At 6 months you can give your baby solids three times a day and start to offer solids before a milk feed. Milk is still an important part of their diet but solids take preference at this age. Don't panic if their milk intake drops a little at this stage as they will be making up for it in their solid diet through custards, yoghurts and cheeses. Daily milk intake should be approximately 600ml. This includes breast/formula and solids that contain milk.

At 6 months you can start to mash your baby's food rather than pureeing it. This helps them to get used to eating lumps. Also, now is the time to start adding finger food to your baby's diet. Providing finger food teaches your baby hand—mouth and hand—eye coordination. It also teaches your baby to bite off and chew, and provides opportunity for fine motor skills to be developed. In addition, your baby learns to eat independently. When you start your baby on finger foods, don't leave them unattended as they can gag while learning to eat the different types of foods you offer. It's important not to offer finger foods that can break off into hard pieces as your baby may choke. For example, pieces of raw apple, carrot and celery need to be grated.

At **6 months** your baby's routine may look like this:

6 months	6–7 am	Milk feed* Breakfast
Times are guidelines only >	11.30–12 md	Lunch Milk feed
	5 pm	Dinner Milk feed
	10 pm	Milk feed
	Remember Allow a break between the meal and the milk feed	

* After sleeping through the night most babies are very thirsty when they wake up in the morning. Most mothers choose to give the milk feed first, before brekkie, but you can do it the other way around if your baby can wait!

At 6 months, the number of milk feeds a day can drop to four.

It will take a week or so for your baby to adjust to the 6-month routine. Once they have settled into the routine, you can add morning and afternoon tea according to their needs. (See page 71 for ideas.)

Here is a sample menu for a day:

Breakfast

Weetbix or similar iron-fortified cereal with mashed fruit.

Toast fingers.

NOTE: mash one Weetbix to a mushy consistency with warm water, which has been boiled. You can add some formula or expressed breast milk if you like.

Mashed fruit ideas: banana, stewed pears or apples.

Toast ideas: spread toast with butter/margarine, vegemite/marmite, avocado or tahini. Try and avoid sweet spreads.

Lunch

Plain/vanilla yoghurt or homemade custard with mashed/pureed fruit.

Sandwiches.

NOTE: try to avoid sweet yoghurt. Refer to recipes on pages 67–70 on how to make custards and fresh fruit toppings.

Sandwiches: when you first introduce sandwiches use a soft brown bread. Avoid the heavy, grainy breads for now as they can be a bit stodgy and hard to swallow. Cut sandwich into fingers, triangles or squares. Refer to recipes on pages 74–77 for sandwich-filling ideas. For more lunch ideas refer to recipes on pages 73–74.

Dinner

Vegies—approximately 1 cup of a mixture of pureed, mashed and soft pieces.

NOTE: Refer to recipes on pages59–60 for vegetable ideas. If your baby is still hungry after the vegies you could give them a small amount of fruit and yoghurt or something similar.

- Introduce these new foods over a period of a week or so. Don't do it all in one day, or it will be a bit overwhelming for your baby.

- When you first introduce toast and sandwiches, you will find your baby won't swallow a lot of the bread, but will suck on it and spit it out producing a pulpy mess. Don't think that they don't like toast and sandwiches. It's all part of the learning-to-eat process. As time goes by, with practice your baby will master biting and chewing and then will start to swallow the food.

- At 6 months your baby can have only the egg yolk, not the whole egg.

Between **6** and **7 months** you can start to add some lentil and bean purees to your baby's vegies. Refer to recipes on pages 62–66 on how to make these.

If your baby has been coping well with this new food routine, at around **8 months** you can start to offer some more challenging food, for example, vegetable patties, pasta and rice. See recipes on pages 80–89 for ideas.

Your baby's palate is bland compared to the sophisticated palate of an adult so you don't need to add ingredients such as sugar, salt and spices to make your baby's or child's food tasty.

At approximately 8 months your baby will be ready to drop the 10 pm milk feed so the solid intake may increase.

By **8–9 months** your baby should be eating mashed and finger foods. Encourage your baby to pick up food from their plate, for example, pieces of soft fruit and pieces of cooked vegies. Also at this age you can start to put a small amount of cow's or soy milk on their breakfast cereal and at 9 months you can start to cook with whole egg.

At around this time you can give your baby a plastic spoon to play with, under supervision, in their highchair at mealtimes. By the age of **10–12 months** they will be attempting to feed themselves with a spoon and, with practice, relatively controlled use of the spoon will occur at around **16–18 months**.

It's important that, once they are showing signs of wanting to feed themselves, you let them do it. Don't fall into the trap of being so concerned about the mess that you want to do it for them. This only delays their independence. Also, it is normal for a baby to play with their food (within reason—you don't want them throwing food around the room). Your baby is learning about the smells, colours and textures of foods. If you let them play, they will go through this phase and get on with the next phase. If you try to stop the playing phase they still have to go through it sometime. I've watched two-year-olds go through the playing phase which they should have got over and done with before 12 months, because their parents have been so worried about the mess.

Here are some ideas on how to manage mealtime mess:

- Buy a special plastic mat or piece of plastic sheeting to go under the highchair to catch all the spills.

- Buy a bib with the arms sewn in or a moulded plastic bib with a lip at the bottom to catch the food.

- Choose a highchair that is easy to clean with a tray that is easy to remove.

- Have plenty of wet washers or cloths on hand.

- If it's a lovely sunny day and you have a shady spot outside, take the highchair out and have a picnic.

- In the evening, bathe your baby after their dinner, not before.

Once your baby reaches **12 months** they can basically eat what you have prepared for the evening meal. You may want to make the transition over a month or so. If your baby has been on a fairly bland diet and you eat rich or spicy meals, introducing adult foods overnight might be a bit of a shock. The following table is a guide to the best age to introduce certain foods:

Food	Age
Rice cereal	4 months
Fruit	4½ months
Vegetables	4½ months
Yoghurt, custard and cheese	6 months
Egg yolk	6 months
Beans and lentils	6–7 months
Cooking with cow's/soy milk	6 months
Small amount of cow's/soy milk on breakfast cereal	8–9 months
Whole egg	9 months
Cow's/soy milk as a drink	12 months
Honey	12 months
Peanut and nut pastes	12 months

MEALTIME TIPS FOR THE OLDER BABY AND TODDLER

Older baby: 12–18 months

- At 12 months your baby can eat what you are preparing for the evening meal.

- Make sure they are strapped in their highchair—at this age they really move fast!

- Presentation is important, make the food colourful and inviting.

- Try not to feed your baby too close to bedtime as they are usually tired and cranky, and may refuse their meal.

- Give them their milk/juice/water after their meal so they don't fill up on liquid first.

- Encourage independent eating. Let them practice with a spoon, under supervision.

Toddler: 18 months–3 years

- From 18 months to 2 years a toddler can start to sit at their own small table. Sit with them at first to encourage them not to walk away.

- Don't encourage them to walk around the room with food, as they risk choking and it sets up negative eating patterns.

- A favourite dolly or teddy sitting on a chair opposite may help.

- Praise your child (a lot) if it's a successful meal sitting.

- When your child is older (at about 3 years) get them involved in preparing their meals.

- Eighteen months to three years is the typical age tantrums can occur, and often happen at mealtimes. Usually it's because your child doesn't want to sit still at the table, or doesn't want to eat the prepared meal. It's important to use a no-fuss technique. Be calm but firm and ignore the tantrum. Take the meal away until they have settled down, then return the meal to the table. Remember, if your child is hungry they won't starve themselves. Toddlers can be finicky with their meals, so don't panic if they miss one. Don't make an issue of it.

- Don't turn yourself inside out offering four different meals at one sitting just to get your toddler to eat something. It's already turned into a game.

- Make sure that the adults set the same limits at mealtimes so your child doesn't get confused with several different rules. It's important that your child experiences continuity.

- Avoid giving continuous snacks throughout the day to your child except for morning and afternoon tea, otherwise they won't be hungry at mealtimes.

- Morning and afternoon tea are important at this age as toddlers are constantly using up energy. Refer pages 71–77 for ideas.

Above all, make mealtimes relaxing and fun. Happy eating!

PRE-PACKAGED BABY FOODS

Pre-packaged or tinned/jar baby foods are very useful when you are travelling or you need something quick and easy in an emergency. I feel, however, when a baby is fed only on these products they miss out on the whole education of eating. They miss out on the true smell of the food and its taste, colours and textures. They don't learn to bite off and chew or learn to eat lumpy food as the jar food doesn't provide these opportunities. Also, their food association is distorted as they don't learn to identify with individual types of food when it is all mixed up together in the jar. The transition to 'normal' food for babies who have been brought up on pre-packaged baby food is very difficult and traumatic for both the baby and the mother as the baby or child basically has to be re-educated to eat and this leads to many tears and tantrums.

If you start your baby off on a good healthy eating pattern, it will set them up for life. They will eat most foods and be more adventurous when trying new foods—making your job a lot easier and making mealtimes fun and stress free.

A NOTE ABOUT FOOD ALLERGIES AND INTOLERANCES

It can be a difficult process to determine whether a child or baby has an allergy or intolerance. Obviously the more pronounced the symptoms, the easier it is to diagnose between an allergy and an intolerance and the more subtle the symptoms, the harder it is to diagnose whether it's an allergy or an intolerance.

A food allergy is an adverse reaction to food involving the immune system of the body. A positive skin prick test administered by an allergist is usually adequate proof of immune system involvement. A food allergy generally begins in childhood.

A food intolerance is an adverse reaction to food but does not involve the immune system. Skin prick tests and other tests for the particular 'allergy' usually return a negative result. A food intolerance can begin at any time of life.

Do not suppose, or worry unduly, that your baby or child will suffer a food allergy unless there is a history of food allergies in the family. If there is, it may be a good idea to talk to your doctor, paediatrician or early child health nurse before commencing solids. The main problem foods for a baby or child on a vegetarian diet can be: cow's milk and dairy products, eggs, nuts, wheat, soy products, and artificial colourings, additives and preservatives.

The common symptoms for a food allergy or intolerance are: rashes, hives or welts—especially around the mouth, face and neck; excessive mucus, stomach pains and bloating; diarrhoea and vomiting; excessive wind or flatus; a runny or congested nose; asthma; sneezing; eczema; and excessive screaming. The older child may complain of a headache, nausea or limb pains. A life-threatening reaction could be an anaphylactic shock, where the airways constrict and the throat and tongue swell, impairing breathing. This usually means the child has a severe allergy and medical attention needs to be sought immediately. Usually, if your baby or child is going to have a severe reaction to food, it will happen shortly after the food is consumed.

It's important when introducing solids to introduce foods one at a time, so you can watch for any reactions and, if there is a reaction, it's easier to detect which food is the culprit. Also, introducing new foods slowly enables your baby's immature and developing digestive system to adjust to the different foods offered.

If your baby or child does react to a certain type of food, you need to withdraw it from their diet for about 2 weeks, then re-introduce it. If they have the same reaction again, you can be pretty sure that food was the culprit. Any severe allergy or intolerance to food should be brought to the attention of your doctor, paediatrician or early child health nurse, who then may refer you to an Allergist. A proper elimination diet should be followed with supervision by health professionals.

It is important from time to time to challenge your baby or child with the problem food to see if the reaction is still there, as their digestive system is maturing as they get older. However, if your child has had a severe reaction to the problem food in the past, re-introduction should be done under medical supervision.

Whether or not your child will grow out of the allergy depends on the type of food they are allergic to. This is something you need to talk to your allergist about.

CONSTIPATION

Breastfed babies usually don't have a problem with being constipated. It's normal for breastfed babies to have frequent bowel motions or to go several days without opening their bowels. Babies who are formula fed are more prone to constipation. Signs to watch out for are straining and, passing small pebble-like stools. Sometimes your baby may pass a little blood from all the straining. If bleeding occurs, you need to get your baby checked by a doctor.

There are several ways to relieve your baby's constipation:

1   Offer some extra cooled boiled water in a bottle, for example, 30 ml between feeds.

2   Put some Maltogen (you can buy this from the chemist) in your baby's bottle. Start off with a teaspoon per bottle. You usually add it just before the feed. It may help to mix the powder in a little boiled water till it is dissolved then add it to formula milk. Use the Maltogen until your baby passes a stool. Recommence the Maltogen again when you feel they are starting to get constipated.

3   Offer your baby some diluted prune juice in a bottle between
    feeds. You can start offering this from about 3 months onwards.
    Start off with 10 ml of prune juice to 30 ml of cooled boiled water,
    working up to half and half—15 ml prune juice to 15 ml cooled
    boiled water. You can use commercially available prune juice or
    make your own. See recipe on page 58 in this book.

Once your baby commences on solids and is eating fruit and
vegies, and later when they are eating a full vegetarian diet, it
would be unlikely that they would get constipated.

If your baby or child is eating meat, constipation may still be
an issue. If this is the case, make some prune pulp (see recipe on
page 58 in this book) and serve with cereal at breakfast time.
Usually a large tablespoon of prune pulp is sufficient.

If none of these options has been of any benefit for your baby
or child, you will need to consult your doctor.

In the Kitchen

STERILISATION AND HYGIENE

Sterilisation and hygiene are very important for your baby's health and wellbeing. A slight cold or mild case of gastroenteritis may not be serious for an adult but it could make a baby very sick. That's why you must take a little extra care when it comes to your baby's feeding equipment and general hygiene.

If your baby is being breastfed, you are lucky in the sterilisation department as you will only need to sterilise the dummy (if you use one) and the occasional bottle or expressing equipment. If your baby is being fed on formula, you have a year of constant sterilising in front of you. You can start to relax the sterilising at **10 months** and cease altogether at **12 months**. However, it's still important after this time to continue to maintain hygiene, making sure you wash your baby's bottles and teats well in warm soapy water using a bottle brush.

Sterilisation

There are three ways to sterilise feeding equipment. All three do the job well but it comes down to personal preference. Whatever method you use, make sure you wash all feeding equipment well in warm soapy water with a bottle brush and rinse it well first. You will get longer use out of feeding equipment if you look after it well and follow the manufacturer's instructions on your sterilising unit.

Boiling

Submerge washed and rinsed bottles, teats and caps in a saucepan of boiling water and boil for 5 minutes. Wait till cool, remove items and drain. You can use plastic and glass bottles with this method.

NOTE: do not use this method in a microwave. There are special microwave steamers available.

Steaming

There are different steaming units on the market. Some are electrical and others are for the microwave. You just place washed and rinsed items in the steamer, put in the appropriate amount of water and turn it on. Usually it takes around 10 minutes. Wait until items are cool before removing them.

Make sure the bottles and other items are washed and rinsed well before placing in steamer. Steamers tend to bake on any leftover residues.

NOTE: be very careful with your steamer as it can burn you if you take the lid off too soon after it's completed its cycle. Be specially careful when removing steaming units from the microwave. I recommend that you leave the steamer in the microwave until it has cooled. Also check the manufacturer's instructions before you buy a steamer if you are going to use glass bottles, as some units are not made to take them. The glass bottles get so hot they can melt the plastic inside the steaming unit.

Chemical sterilisation

There are different varieties of chemical units available. Basically, you fill the unit with water to the marked level and add the appropriate amount of sterilising tablets or liquid. You need to submerge the washed and rinsed items completely. Usually a plunger is provided. The equipment needs to stay in the solution for an hour and the solution needs to be changed every 24 hours. You can use plastic or glass bottles with this method.

Make sure the bottles and other items are rinsed well as the soap could counteract the sterilising solution.

NOTE: you can't put metal items into the solution as they will corrode. You do not need to rinse solution off the equipment when it is sterilised. The manufacturers claim it is safe for your baby. If your baby objects to the taste or smell, you can rinse the equipment off with cooled boiled water.

If you choose the chemical or steaming method follow the manufacturer's instructions carefully. After any of the sterilising methods described here you can assemble the bottle and pop it in the fridge, making sure the teat is covered, and it will remain sterile for 24 hours.

Hygiene

Here are some ways you can maintain hygiene in the kitchen:

- Clean and wipe down bench tops before making formula and preparing expressed breast milk, solids and meals.

- Wash your hands before attending to formula making, and preparing expressed breast milk, solids and meals.

- When making up formula, make sure the water has boiled properly and follow instructions on back of tin carefully.

- If you have a cold, avoid coughing or sneezing over formula or foods. Wash your hands after blowing your nose.

- If you have any cuts or infections on your hands, wear suitable rubber gloves.

- Keep the kitchen clean and tidy.

- Empty rubbish bins regularly.

- When dishcloths are starting to look soiled, change them.

- Change tea-towels regularly. Have a handtowel in the kitchen as well, so people are not wiping their hands on the tea-towel.

- Keep pets away from areas of food preparation.

For more information relating to hygiene refer to the following section on preparing and storing meals.

PREPARING AND STORING MEALS

The preparation and storage of food is an important part of the cooking process. The way in which you shop, prepare, cook and store your food will determine how much nutritional value the food retains. Careful planning of food shopping, preparation, cooking and storage will save you time and money.

Preparation

Shopping

Here are some shopping tips:

- Take a list with you, it will save you time and ensure that you don't buy too many extras.

- Make a habit of checking all food labels for use-by dates and storage instructions before you buy.

- Check use-by dates on 'specials' as they may be nearing the end of their storage life.

- Buy the freshest looking fruit and vegies—you want to get maximum storage life.

- Don't buy:

  - Swollen chilled-food packages, for example, fruit juices, unprocessed cheeses, yoghurt and made-up pastry. When the packages are swollen, the contents are 'going off'.

- Swollen, dented, leaking canned food or canned foods with external rusting.

- Dairy products and delicatessen items that are kept outside a refrigerated cabinet.

- Frozen foods that have been stored above the 'load line' in the frozen food display cabinets. The 'load line' is usually 5 cm below the rim of the freezer.

- Frozen food packs containing ice crystals or packets with clumps of ice between them. Both conditions indicate re-freezing and probably loss of quality.

- Foods in torn packages or with imperfect seals.

- Avoid overbuying chilled foods because of their limited shelf life.

- Don't leave chilled or frozen foods sitting in your car for longer than necessary. If you have a long trip home, take an insulated container with you, for example, an esky with travel iceblocks to transport the food home.

- As soon as you get home, pack away the chilled and frozen foods in your fridge and freezer.

If you are in a situation where your baby or child can be minded while you go to the supermarket or fruit and vegie shop, it will make the excursion a lot easier. If this is not possible, it's a good idea not to take hungry or tired babies or children shopping. It's better to give them their meals before you go, otherwise you will have cranky, demanding children on your hands, maybe pulling food off the shelves. A tired baby will not tolerate waiting in a queue, bright lights and crowds of people milling around.

Food preparation

The biggest factor in the preparation of meals is having the time, which can be hard in a busy household. I have always found the best time to cook is when my charges are asleep.

Here are some helpful tips:

- The day before you plan to cook, buy all the ingredients you need so that as soon as your baby's head hits the pillow you are ready to start.

- Cook in bulk so you are not cooking every day. (See storage information, page 36.) Start off with a clean kitchen. There is nothing more disheartening than finishing up a cooking session, the baby starts to wake and you have the dishes from last night, breakfast and your most recent cooking session to deal with.

- Before you start, wash your hands and wipe down the benches.

- If your child is older and not sleeping as much in the day, make sure they have an activity to keep them occupied so they are not getting under your feet.

- If your child is over 3 years old, get them involved in some small way.

- Check use-by dates on food before cooking, and use fresh fruit and vegies, not the ones that have been sitting in the back of the fridge for weeks. (Refer to storage information, page 36.)

- Make sure you wash all fruit and vegies well as this may help to remove any residues from pesticides.

- To minimise vitamin C loss from your fruit and vegies, don't wash, peel, cut or grate them until you are ready to start cooking.

Cooking

Any form of cooking will result in a loss of some nutrients but the losses can be kept to a minimum. Steaming and microwaving food, especially vegetables, are good ways of retaining most of the nutrients. To avoid uneven cooking in the microwave, observe the manufacturer's instructions for stirring and standing times.

When boiling your vegies, water-soluble vitamins such as B and C are easily lost by leaching into the cooking water. To minimise this, don't add the vegies until the water has boiled and don't overcook them. Since the cooking water contains some vitamins, use it to make soups and sauces instead of pouring it down the sink.

Stir frying, which might not be suitable for your child until they are older, retains the vegetables' crispness and nutrients as well as ensuring the minimal absorption of oil.

Equipment

There are a few items that I have found invaluable in the kitchen:

- A chopping board made of glass or plastic, which is easy to clean and more hygienic

- Kitchen knives that can easily cut through all types of fruit and vegies

- A good fruit and vegetable peeler

- Microwave dishes or a steamer insert for the saucepan for vegies

- A colander (strainer)

- A masher and a grater

- A Bamix or a similar type of upright blender—you need a large beaker or tall plastic jug to blend food in

- Lots of small-to-medium sized plastic storage containers with fitting lids

- A deep ice cube tray

- Labels

- A non-stick frying pan

- A good set of saucepans

Storage

Storing food in the fridge

Refrigeration can substantially reduce the rate at which food will deteriorate. Low temperatures slow down the growth of micro-organisms and the rate of chemical (including enzymic) changes in food. These are the two main causes of food spoilage. Your fridge should be maintained at a temperature between 0–5°C. A refrigerator thermometer can help you to check this. In most of the newer style fridges, the temperature will be the same throughout. With the older styles you may find the upper shelves cooler than the lower shelves.

Here are some refrigeration hints:

- Avoid overcrowding and allow air to circulate around each item.

- Remember the door is the warmest part of the fridge. Store items that don't perish quickly or those that will be used quickly, for example, milk and orange juice.

- Foods with strong odours should be covered.

- Keep opened dairy products covered as they can absorb flavours and odours from other foods in the fridge.

- Check use-by dates regularly.

- Throw out food that is going off, as it can taint other foods.

- Clean out your refrigerator regularly.

Leftovers, if maintained at a temperature of 0–5°C in the fridge, can be kept for 3 days. This includes cooked fruit and vegies that you prepare for your baby's solids. After 3 days leftovers should be thrown out.

Storing food in the freezer

Keeping your freezer at or below −18°C almost completely stops food deterioration. Each food group has a recommended maximum storage time—after this it slowly starts to deteriorate. Check the inside of your freezer door and the manufacturer's instructions to determine how long each type of food can be stored in your freezer. Also check the recommended storage time and the required temperature on the store-bought frozen packet.

Generally speaking, cooked and uncooked fruit and vegetables can be safely frozen for 6 months. Such foods will probably be okay in 12 months' time, but because the history of the food before you bought it is unknown to you — for example how long has it been in cold storage — 6 months is a good guideline. People who freeze their own garden produce could freeze the product longer than 6 months because they know the full history of the vegetable or fruit.

Nutrients are generally retained well during freezing. To get maximum nutritional value out of your frozen food, it's a good idea to label and date everything that goes into the freezer so you can keep track of what's recent and what's very old.

Defrost the freezer part of your fridge or the freezer itself regularly. Too much ice build-up reduces the freezer's efficiency. (This does not apply to automatic-defrost models.)

It's probably a good idea not to overcrowd or cram your domestic freezer with huge amounts of food for long periods of time unless you have a freezer in peak condition. A completely separate freezer like a chest or upright type will cope better with larger amounts of food.

Dehydrated and dried foods

Dried foods undergo slow chemical changes that lead to their gradual loss of quality. This is accelerated by high temperatures and exposure to the air, especially moist air. It's important to read storage instructions and use-by dates on the food packaging. Store dehydrated and dried foods in a cool dry place away from sources of heat such as the oven and the dishwasher or direct sunlight. Once the packet is opened, place the unused portion in an airtight container.

The main problem with dried foods is insect infestation. You should check your stored dried foods regularly for this. Foods with mould growth should not be eaten as the mould may be toxic. Mould on dried food should not occur unless it has been exposed to moisture.

Canned food

During processing, the contents of canned foods are sterilised, so if the food has been properly processed spoilage by microbes does not occur. Over time, slow chemical changes do occur. There is no sudden change from acceptability to non-acceptability, but changes in colour, texture and flavour develop to the point that the food doesn't taste as good as it should. The vitamin content of canned food does decrease over time.

Canned food should be stored in a cool place—usually a pantry is ideal. Watch for swollen or leaky cans. It is recommended that you clean out your canned foods every 12 months so that you are getting maximum quality and nutritional value out of them. Although many canned foods will keep longer, because of the uncertainty as to the true age of the food, a 12-month maximum should be set. Canned rhubarb, fruit juice, soft drinks and some baby foods are exceptions and have a maximum storage life of about 6 months.

Once the can has been opened, treat the contents as you would treat fresh food of the same kind. Unused portions of the canned food should be placed in a container with a lid and placed in the fridge. If it is stored in the open tin, the food will take on a metallic taste.

Fruit and vegetables

Here are a few tips on storing fruit and vegetables:

- Handle fresh fruit and vegetables carefully. Bruising and breakages of the skin will encourage deterioration and rotting.

- Some produce, especially produce from the tropics, for example, pineapples and bananas, is chill-sensitive and should not be stored in the fridge.

- Keep leafy vegetables and root vegetables, for example carrots and parsnips, in a perforated plastic bag in the fridge to reduce water loss and therefore prevent wilting.

- Remove leafy tops from carrots, parsnips, turnips and beetroot. This will extend their storage life in the fridge for many weeks.

- Store potatoes and sweet potatoes in a paper bag, or a box, or in a wire or plastic bin, in a cool, dark, well-ventilated place to avoid potatoes greening and sprouting.

- Keep nectarines, pears, peaches, and plums in the fridge unless you want to ripen them.

- Tomatoes can be ripened at room temperature away from direct sunlight, as can rockmelons, pineapples, paw paw, bananas, mangoes, avocados, stonefruit and pears. They will not ripen in the fridge. Once they are ripened to your liking, you can store them in the fridge.

For more information on storing fruit and vegetables in the home refer to the information overleaf.

Optimum storage conditions and approximate storage life for fresh fruit and vegetables in the home

Shelf life	Coldest part of refrigerator	Warmer part of refrigerator	In a cool place in the home
very short shelf life – often less than 1 week	apricots	paw paw (ripe)	bananas (ripe)
	asparagus		basil (stems in water)
	avocados (ripe)		custard apples (unripe)
	blackberries		mango (unripe)
	cherries		nectarines (unripe)
	custard apples (ripe)		paw paw (unripe)
	figs		peaches (unripe)
	green peas		pumpkin (immature)
	guavas		rambutan
	herbs (most types)		rockmelon (whole)
	honeydew melon (cut)		squash (immature)
	leafy vegetables		starfruit
	loquats		
	lychees		
	mushrooms		
	nectarines (ripe)		
	peaches		

Shelf life	Coldest part of refrigerator	Warmer part of refrigerator	In a cool place in the home
very short shelf life – often less than 1 week	pears (ripe)		
	persimmons (ripe)		
	plums, juicy e.g. Narrabeen (ripe)		
	raspberries		
	rockmelon (cut)		
	shallots		
	spring onions		
	strawberries		
	watermelon (cut)		
short shelf life – 1 week	blueberries	capsicum	bananas (green)
	broccoli	chilli	cucumber
	chestnuts	green beans	eggplant
	grapes	mango (ripe)	lettuce, hydroponic in water
	lettuce	pumpkin (cut)	pineapple
	passionfruit		tomatoes
	plums, drier e.g. President		watermelon (whole)
	red radish (topped)		zucchini
	rhubarb		
	sweet corn		

Shelf life	Coldest part of refrigerator	Warmer part of refrigerator	In a cool place in the home
medium shelf life – 2 weeks	apples – most varieties	grapefruit	avocados (firm)
	Brussels sprouts	lemons	
	cabbage (cut)	limes	
	carrots (topped)	mandarins	
	celery	oranges	
	kohlrabi		
	pears (unripe)		
	persimmons (unripe)		
	turnips		
	white radish		
longer shelf life – 3–4 weeks	apples – Granny Smith & Fuji		garlic
	beetroot (topped)		lemon grass
	cabbage (whole)		honeydew melon (whole)
	Chinese cabbage		onions
	parsnips		potatoes (in the dark)
	quinces		pumpkin (mature, whole)
			squash (mature, whole)
			sweet potatoes

The information in this table is reproduced with the permission of Food Science Australia from the fact sheet *Refrigerated storage of perishable foods*.

Eggs

Eggs can cause food poisoning if they are not stored correctly, so following are a few helpful notes on eggs:

- Most supermarkets do not refrigerate eggs, so make sure they are stored in the coolest part of the store. If they aren't, do not buy them, go elsewhere.

- Put the eggs into the fridge as soon as you get home from the shops.

- Eggs are porous so keep eggs in the cartons you bought them in. Don't put them in the special holders in the fridge door. The cartons reduce water loss from the eggs and help prevent flavours from other foods being absorbed into the eggs.

- The expected storage life for eggs in the shell is determined by the storage temperature during distribution.

- If you have your own chooks, freshly laid eggs should be put into cartons straightaway and stored in the fridge. Only clean and uncracked eggs should be stored. If you adhere to these guidelines and the refrigerator temperature is maintained at 0–5°C, the eggs will store for 3 months.

- Dirty or cracked eggs should be used as soon as possible. Washing the eggs removes the surface bloom and makes them more susceptible to attack by microbes.

- Here is a quick way to test an egg's freshness. Place the raw egg in its shell in a basin of water. Fresh eggs stay at the bottom of the bowl, while stale eggs float to the top. When it's cracked open, the yolk of a fresh egg is small and rounded, and stands high in the egg white. The yolk of a stale egg is large and flat, and tends to break from its rounded shape into a runny liquid. Of course, the smell will alert you to an egg's freshness .

- Remember, do not offer your baby egg yolk until they are 6 months old. And do not offer the whole egg (yolk and white) until your baby is 9 months old.

Thawing and reheating

Thawing and re-heating food needs careful attention, as these are the times when food spoilage can occur. Here are some helpful guidelines:

- Once frozen food has been thawed, do not re-freeze it.

- If food is thawed in the fridge, it can be safely stored for up to 48 hours.

- If food in the freezer starts to thaw due to a rise in temperature, chemical and microbiological activity will be stimulated and spoilage may result. A rise in temperature may occur if the electricity is turned off or the freezer is malfunctioning.

- Put freshly cooked leftovers in the fridge straightaway. Modern refrigerators can cope with small amounts of hot food. If there is a large amount of food left over, do not let it cool on the bench for longer than 1 hour.

- When heating leftovers, make sure the food reaches 75°C throughout.

- Don't reheat leftovers more than once. The repeated heating and cooling of food destroys vitamins and encourages bacterial growth.

- Leftovers, if stored in the correct conditions, should be eaten within approximately 3 days.

Ways to avoid food poisoning

Food poisoning is not as likely to occur in a vegetarian home as in a meat-eating household but care should be taken because it can still happen.

- Wash your hands before preparing meals!

- Avoid excessive handling of food. Make sure utensils, crockery and serving dishes are clean.

- Make sure dairy products are stored at the correct temperature, 0–5°C.

- Place cooked meals on the shelves in the fridge above raw foods.

- Check eggs for use-by dates before cooking with them. If you're not sure, don't use them!

- Serve foods such as salads, and desserts and cakes containing cream or imitation cream, direct from the fridge. Do not allow these foods to sit on the table for hours before eating.

- Have a handtowel in kitchen as well as a tea-towel. This will help stop bacteria being passed from hands to clean dishes.

- Food kept at temperatures between 4°C and 60°C is the danger zone, because this is the temperature range in which food-poisoning bacteria may grow. Refer to the picture of the thermometer.

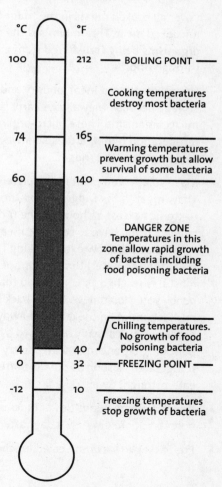

°C | °F

100 — 212 — BOILING POINT —

Cooking temperatures destroy most bacteria

74 — 165

Warming temperatures prevent growth but allow survival of some bacteria

60 — 140

DANGER ZONE
Temperatures in this zone allow rapid growth of bacteria including food poisoning bacteria

Chilling temperatures. No growth of food poisoning bacteria

4 — 40

0 — 32 — FREEZING POINT —

-12 — 10

Freezing temperatures stop growth of bacteria

A note about meat

I realise that many people will refer to this book for vegetarian meals to supplement their child's meat diet, so, even though this is a vegetarian book, I feel the following points regarding food poisoning are too important to leave out.

- Be particularly careful not to undercook chicken, pork or fish.

- Never handle cooked and uncooked meats together. Do not use the same utensils or chopping boards.

- Cover all cooked meats in the fridge and store them above uncooked meat. This minimises the risk of food-poisoning organisms being transferred from uncooked to cooked meat through drips.

- Uncooked minced meat, poultry and seafoods need careful storage because they always carry large numbers of spoilage micro-organisms. These micro-organisms can grow even at refrigeration temperatures, so always store these foods in the coldest part of the fridge.

- Make sure frozen meat is completely thawed before cooking. Thaw meat in the fridge to stop the growth of food-poisoning bacteria. At least 24 hours in the fridge should be all that is needed. If you have to cook the meat, for example a roast, before it has thawed, allow extra cooking time. Ensure (by using a good meat thermometer) that the temperature in the middle of the roast has reached 75°C. If you do thaw meat, poultry or fish on the bench you should never put it back into the fridge to be used later on. If it cannot be cooked right away, it should be thrown out because it has already developed a large population of food-poisoning organisms. Meat, poultry and seafoods must be refrigerated as soon as possible after cooking if they are not to be eaten straight away.

- Only buy small quantities of luncheon meats at a time as they only last approximately 4 days after purchase.

- Pre-packaged vacuum-sealed luncheon meats have a longer shelf life.

- All luncheon meats, including salami, should be refrigerated at all times.

- If you are sending your children off to school with luncheon meats in their sandwiches, include a cold pack in their lunchbox to keep the contents cool. Otherwise, make sure your child is keeping their schoolbag somewhere cool—not outside in the sun!

Making and storing solids

You have several choices when it comes to making and storing your baby's solids and meals:

1   You can make up fresh fruit and vegetables every day, though this can be very time consuming as your baby needs only small amounts.

2   You can cook in bulk and freeze. Deep ice-cube trays are great for fruit and vegetable purees when your baby is first starting on solids, as each section is a perfect portion. You will need to cover the tray with foil or place it in a large freezer bag and seal the bag. Then you just pop out a portion as needed. As your baby gets older and the portions get larger, you can start to store the purees in small storage containers. Don't forget to label and date them! The more challenging foods, patties, and rice, pasta and lentil dishes, freeze well in separate portions. You could cook a month's worth of meals in several sessions.

3   You can make fresh fruit and vegie purees every 3 days and keep them in separate small containers in the fridge. The purees will remain safe to eat for 3 days as long as your fridge is operating at a temperature of 0–5°C. After 3 days discard the solids. Don't forget to label and date the containers so you can keep track of the age of the food.

4   You could do a combination of fresh and frozen food, for example, make up fresh vegies every 3 days and keep them in fridge, and store the savouries that go with the vegies, for instance, patties, in the freezer.

NOTE: when taking food out of the freezer, try and plan ahead. Take your baby's dinner out in the morning and put it in fridge so it can defrost over the day. Do not leave the food on the bench all day to defrost. If you choose to place a frozen meal in the microwave, make sure it heats evenly right through.

Storing expressed breast milk (EBM)

To get the optimum nutritional value from your expressed breast milk for your baby you should do the following:

- Breast milk must be expressed into a sterile container or bottle and then stored in a sterile container or plastic bottle, or special EBM storage bags. Sterile containers with screw-top lids and EBM storage bags can be purchased from a pharmacy.

- Do not fill the sterile container or bottle right up to the top as the milk will expand when it freezes and burst the container or bottle. Fill containers and bottles to only three-quarters full.

- It is very important that you label your EBM with the date and time that you expressed.

- Fresh EBM stores in the fridge for 24 hours. After 24 hours it must be thrown out.

- On the completion of the feed, the leftover EBM must be thrown out.

- EBM stores for 2 weeks in a freezer compartment inside the fridge.

- EBM stores for 3 months in the freezer section of the fridge with its own separate door.

- EBM stores for 6 months in the deep freeze, for example, chest or upright freezer that is separate from the fridge. The temperature must be −18°C or lower.

- If you have a limited number of storage containers you can add fresh EBM to EBM that is already frozen if the fresh EBM is chilled in the fridge first. Never add warm EBM to frozen EBM.

- Do not use the microwave to heat the EBM. Research suggests that microwaving can change the immunological and nutrient quality of the milk.

- Do not leave the EBM on the bench to thaw. The aim when defrosting EBM is to do it quickly. Stand the container of frozen EBM in a jug of warm-to-hot water, but not boiling water as it may curdle the milk. You need to heat the milk only to body temperature—that's the temperature of the milk your baby gets when feeding from the breast.

- If you thaw the frozen EBM in the fridge, it will be safe to use within 24 hours. After 24 hours it must be thrown out.

- Don't forget to use the oldest EBM in the freezer first.

Making up formula

There are several ways of making up formula:

1 Make up each feed in the bottle as you need it.

2 Make up all the feeds you need for the next 24 hours in one go in separate bottles.

3 Make up all the feeds you need for the next 24 hours in one go in a sterile jug, and pour the feeds as you go.

Storing formula

There are certain guidelines that need to be followed for storing formula as it has a brief storage life:

- Check the use-by date on the tin before buying formula.

- Once the tin has been opened, its contents have a storage life of only a month. After 1 month it must be thrown out. Make sure the lid is always securely placed on the tin of formula.

- The tin of formula should be stored in a clean, dry place, preferably in a cupboard away from direct heat.

- Made-up formula must be stored in sterile bottles, or in a sterile jug if you are pouring as you go. (Refer to the section on sterilising on page 29.)

- Once the formula has been made up, it must be stored in the fridge. Label formula with the date and time it was made. It has a shelf life of 24 hours. After 24 hours it must be discarded.

- Once your baby's feed is finished the leftover milk in the bottle must be discarded.

- Try to avoid heating the bottle in the microwave. The formula heats from inside to out and if not tested properly before giving to your baby, scalding can occur. The best way is to place the bottle of formula in a jug of hot water and allow to heat to lukewarm. You don't need to give it to them hot. Test the milk on the inside of your arm before giving to your baby.

- You cannot freeze formula!

  NOTE: the formula will heat more quickly in glass bottles than plastic ones.

SAFETY

Maintaining a safe environment in the kitchen for both you and your family is important. Accidents, including drowning, suffocation, burns, falls and poisoning, are the biggest killers of children aged 1–14 in Australia today (Kidsafe, Child Accident Prevention Foundation of Australia). Accidents in the kitchen occur mostly during preparation of meals, especially in the evening when everyone is a bit tired. The hazards are burns and scalds, fire, poisoning, falls and slipping, lacerations and electrocution.

Here are some ways to avoid the hazards:

- Provide an activity for your baby or child to do while you're in the kitchen. It's important that they're not under your feet.

- If you can't keep your child from coming into the kitchen, you may need to put a gate across the kitchen entrance or put them in a playpen.

- Position yourself in the kitchen so you can see into the play area.

- Both electric and gas hotplate and oven controls should not be accessible to children. If the oven is on, keep the children out of the kitchen or teach them very early on not to touch.

- If you have a wood stove, rules must be set early with your children.

- Make sure saucepan handles are turned away from the front of stove so children can't pull the saucepan onto themselves.

- Don't allow cords of appliances such as the kettle, the iron or the toaster to hang down over the bench as children are likely to pull on them.

- Put cups of hot drinks well away from the reach of your child. Never sit your child on your lap while you are having a hot drink.

- Make sure the microwave is not within easy access for children to try and use it by themselves.

- Be careful if you are heating formula in the microwave. Shake the container well and test the formula before giving to your baby.

- Be careful not to overheat your baby or child's solids or meals. Test the temperature before giving the food to them.

- Keep steaming units well out of reach of children.

- Don't encourage children to sit on the bench next to you while you are cooking.

- Make sure there are no stools or chairs close to kitchen benches that a child could climb up on, when your back is turned, and have access to items that burn.

- Make sure the hot-water tap is firmly turned off. Special childproof caps can be bought to fit over the top of the tap.

- Have a fire blanket or small extinguisher in a accessible place in the kitchen.

- Put matches and lighters out of reach.

- Keep poisons out of reach of children! Lock all medicines and poisons in a cupboard or cabinet above bench height.

- Put childproof locks on kitchen cupboards especially the cupboards under the sink and in the laundry where household cleaning products are stored.

- Buy medicines and household products with childproof caps where possible. Toddlers (aged 1–3 years) are at the most risk of poisoning. The poison or medication is often found by your child when it's just been purchased or it is out for use, often on a table or bench. Poisonings usually occur quickly when an adult has left the room.

- Keep poison information number by the phone.

- Wipe up any spills on floors straightaway.

- Make sure when your child is in the highchair at mealtimes that they are strapped in and are not left unattended.

- Fit childproof locks on your drawers that contain knives and any other sharp utensils, and on cupboards that contain crockery.

- Protruding corners on your kitchen benches should have corner protectors attached.

- Fit plug-in covers on your power points.

- Use electrical safety switches. These turn the power off when there is a fault before people are electrocuted. They are installed by an electrician to your switchboard. Or, instead, plug-in safety switches can be used in each power point.

- Keep a basic first-aid kit handy and brush up on your first-aid skills.

Choking on food

Babies and children are prone to choking so here are some ways you can minimise this:

- Don't leave your baby or child alone when eating.

- Provide age-appropriate foods, for example, raw apple or carrot needs to be grated or cooked for babies.

- Do not allow your child to move around while eating. Encourage them to sit still.

- Do not force-feed your child.

- Do not give popcorn, nuts, hard lollies, corn chips or other similar foods to babies and young children.

- Read up and learn how to administer first-aid to your baby or child if they happen to choke on food.

If you want more information on safety in the home, contact 'Kidsafe' the Child Accident Prevention Foundation in your state or territory.

Recipes

STEWED FRUIT AND VEGIES

Stewed Apples or Pears

Prune Juice

Prune Pulp

Cooked Pumpkin or Sweet Potato

Stewed fruit

A general rule is for babies aged **4–6 months** is that all fruit should be stewed or steamed, except for banana, avocado and tinned fruit. Babies aged **over 6 months** can have fruit in its raw state if it is ripe. Any green/unripe fruit should still be stewed as it may cause a tummy ache.

Stewed Apples or Pears

3–4 granny smith apples or 3-4 pears

➤ Peel, core and slice fruit and place in a small saucepan with enough water to cover bottom of saucepan. You do not need to add sugar. Bring water to the boil on medium heat, then reduce the heat and allow mixture to simmer gently until fruit is soft. A lid on the saucepan will quicken the process. Check regularly for dryness—a little more water can be added if this happens. Once fruit is soft, remove saucepan from heat and allow to cool. Drain off excess water and puree fruit. Freeze stewed fruit in separate portions or store in fridge. (Refer to section on storage of food, page 36.)

Green pears take a little longer to stew than apples. Obviously, the softer the fruit, the less time it takes to stew.

You can try the stewing process for peaches, apricots, and nectarines. Once your baby has tried a wide variety of fruit and has shown no allergies, you can start to combine different fruits.

Here are some yummy combinations to get you started:

Apple and Pear

Pear and Kiwi Fruit

Apple and Mango

Apple and Strawberry

Peach and Nectarine

Apple and Nectarine

Apple and Apricot

Apple and Peach

Apricot and Peach

Banana and Kiwi Fruit

Banana and Paw Paw

Apple and Passionfruit

Apple and Raspberry

Apple and Rhubarb

Preparing tinned fruit

Tinned fruit is an alternative to stewed fruit. Depending on the season, some fruits may not be available or they may be too expensive. Tinned fruit is also quick and easy for those of you whose time is limited. Make sure the tinned fruit you buy is in its natural juice or water with no added sugar. The only tinned fruit I don't recommend are tinned apples, as fresh apples are generally available, so you can make up your own.

To prepare tinned fruit, drain the fruit, then puree it. Freeze pureed fruit in separate portions or store in the fridge.

Prune pulp and prune juice

Prune pulp and prune juice are recommended for babies who are constipated. You can give the prune juice to babies aged **3 months** and over and prune pulp to babies from **6 months** onwards.

Prune Pulp

6–8 prunes

► Place prunes in a small saucepan and add enough water to just cover them. Bring water to the boil, then reduce heat and simmer until prunes are soft. Remove pan from heat and allow to cool.

► Drain prunes, then puree or mash them. Store pulp in a clean container and keep in fridge.

The prune pulp will store for 3 days.
The best way to serve it is to place 1 tablespoon of pulp on your child's breakfast cereal every 1–2 days.

Prune Juice

6–8 prunes

► Place prunes in a small saucepan and add enough water to just cover them. Bring water to the boil, then reduce heat and simmer until prunes are soft. Remove pan from heat and allow to cool.

► Strain the liquid through a sieve, place in a sterile bottle and store in fridge.

Store prune juice for no longer than 3 days. When you first introduce prune juice to your baby, dilute 10 ml prune juice in 30 ml of cooled boiled water, working up to 15 ml prune juice to 15 ml of cooled boiled water. Diluted prune juice can be given once a day between milk feeds. Cease using prune juice when your baby is no longer constipated.

Cooked vegies

Cooked Pumpkin or Sweet Potato

1 small piece of pumpkin, about 500 g, or 1 small- to medium-sized
  sweet potato, about 500 g

► Peel pumpkin, remove seeds, and cut into pieces. Peel and slice
sweet potato.

► Here are three ways to prepare these vegetables:

Microwave

You can now buy special microwavable steaming dishes, which are
great. These usually consist of a container with a basket insert and
a lid. Cover bottom of container with a little water, and place the
pumpkin or sweet potato inside, put on a lid, and place container
in the microwave. The newer microwaves come with a vegetable
sensor button which provides a helpful guide on how long to cook
the vegies for. If you don't have this, cook on high for 2–3 minutes
and check every minute or so until vegies are soft.

Steam

Fill saucepan with water until it just reaches the holes on the
bottom of the steamer insert. Place the pumpkin or sweet potato
inside, put on lid and steam until soft. Check regularly that water
has not dried up on bottom of saucepan. You may need to add a
little more water during steaming process.

Boil

Fill saucepan with water, bring to the boil and add the pumpkin or
sweet potato and check regularly to avoid overcooking. Boil until
vegies are soft.

➤ Once vegetables have cooled, drain and then puree them. You can freeze them in separate portions or store them in the fridge. You do not need to add salt or butter to the cooked vegies. Refer to the section on storage on page 32.

NOTE: sweet potato can be orange or white in colour. I've used orange sweet potato (kumara). The white sweet potato (which is purple in the centre) is much sweeter than the orange variety when cooked.

Any of the above processes can be repeated with vegies such as parsnip, carrot and potato. For the more delicate vegies such as zucchini, baby squash, broccoli, spinach or cauliflower, I recommend steaming or microwaving. Once your baby has tried a wide range of vegetables and has shown no allergies, you can start to combine different vegetables to add some variety.

Here are some tasty combinations:

Zucchini and Baby Yellow Squash

Zucchini and Parsnip

Carrot and Parsnip

Parsnip and Baby Yellow Squash

Sweet Potato and Carrot

Sweet Potato and Pumpkin

Pumpkin and Carrot

Potato and Broccoli

Potato and Spinach

Potato and Parsnip

Broccoli and Zucchini

Broccoli and Baby Yellow Squash

VEGIES WITH FLAIR

Baked Bean Mash

Cauliflower and Carrot Cream

Cauliflower and Creamed Corn Cheese

Mashed Potato with Lentils and Gravy

Eggplant and Tomato

Parsnip with Chickpeas and Gravy

Bean and Tomato Puree

Lentil Puree

Once your baby is **6 months** old you can start to jazz up those vegies. Also, at 6 months, your baby's iron stores start to decrease slowly, so I've included some recipes with lentils and beans that contain high levels of iron as well as protein.

The following recipes make approximately 5 meals for your baby. The meals can be frozen or stored in the fridge for 3 days.

Baked Bean Mash

3 medium-sized potatoes, peeled and cut into chunks

130 g tin baked beans

➤ Steam, microwave or boil potatoes until they are soft. Drain and then mash potatoes with baked beans.

NOTE: baked beans can be given on their own, mashed at first. Later, the whole beans can be served as an accompaniment with vegies for dinner or on their own for lunch. You can also use soy beans in a tomato sauce instead of baked beans. These are available in the health food section at the supermarket.

Cauliflower and Carrot Cream

¼ cauliflower, cut into pieces

2–3 carrots, peeled and sliced

WHITE SAUCE

1 tablespoon butter, margarine or dairy-free margarine

1 tablespoon plain flour or cornflour

1 cup milk or soy milk

➤ Steam carrot and cauliflower until soft.

➤ While vegies are cooking make up white sauce. Melt butter in a small saucepan on medium heat. Remove from heat and add flour and mix to a paste. Add milk and whisk until well combined.

Return to heat and allow mixture to boil, whisking all the time. When sauce thickens, remove pan from heat.

► Puree or mash cauliflower and carrot together. Then slowly pour in the white sauce and mix until you reach the consistency required.

NOTE: for a different taste you could add ¼ cup grated cheese to the white sauce after removing pan from heat.

Cauliflower and Creamed Corn Cheese

½ cauliflower, cut into pieces

130 g tin creamed corn

WHITE SAUCE

1 tablespoon butter, margarine or dairy-free margarine

1 tablespoon plain flour or cornflour

1 cup milk or soy milk

¼ cup grated cheese

► Steam cauliflower until tender.

► While cauliflower is cooking make up white sauce. Melt butter in a small saucepan on medium heat. Remove from heat and add flour and mix to a paste. Add milk and whisk until well combined. Allow mixture to boil, whisking all the time. When sauce thickens, remove pan from heat. Stir in grated cheese and mix until melted.

► Mash or puree cauliflower and mix in creamed corn. Slowly add in white sauce until you reach the consistency required.

NOTE: you can make this recipe without the cheese. For older babies and children, don't mash the cauliflower but leave it in small pieces. Mix the creamed corn into the white sauce and pour over the cauliflower. Creamed corn can be given on its own or mixed with other vegetables.

Mashed Potato with Lentils and Gravy

3 medium potatoes, peeled and cut into chunks

¼ cup red, green or brown lentils

1 tablespoon Massel gravy powder

► Steam potatoes until soft. Mash potatoes and set aside.

► Cook lentils in boiling water on medium to high heat until tender. Drain and set aside.

► Place 1 cup of water in a small saucepan and add gravy powder. Whisk until well combined, allow mixture to boil and thicken, then remove pan from heat.

► Add enough gravy to lentils to make a sloppy consistency. Add lentil mixture to mashed potatoes and mix until well combined. Add extra gravy to potatoes to get desired consistency.

NOTE: for a different taste use sweet potato instead of ordinary potato.

Eggplant and Tomato

1 small eggplant, sliced

olive oil

butter

1 spring onion, chopped

2 tomatoes, peeled and chopped (see instructions below)

¼ cup chopped parsley

► Brush eggplant slices very lightly with olive oil. Place slices on a tray, put under grill and cook until brown on both sides. Allow to cool. Puree eggplant slices and set aside.

▶ Place a little butter in a small saucepan, add spring onion and fry lightly on medium heat until soft. Add tomatoes and a couple tablespoons of water, and simmer for about 10 minutes. Mix in parsley. After a few minutes, mix in pureed eggplant and combine well. You will need to add ¼–½ cup of water at this stage as the eggplant will absorb the liquid. Cook gently for a few more minutes. The mixture should be soft and mushy.

▶ Remove pan from heat and, when mixture has cooled, store in the fridge.

NOTE: you can serve this on its own or serve with cooked rice, lentils or couscous. To make a pasta sauce, add more water (about ⅓ cup) when you add the tomatoes.

PEELING TOMATOES

▶ Cut a small cross on base of tomato. Drop tomatoes into a saucepan of boiling water and boil for 30 seconds. Take out and then place tomatoes in a bowl of very cold water for 30 seconds. Take tomatoes out and peel.

Parsnip with Chickpeas and Gravy

2 parsnips, peeled and sliced

300 g tin chickpeas

1 tablespoon Massel gravy powder

▶ Place 1 cup of water in a small saucepan on medium heat and add gravy powder. Whisk mixture until well combined, allow to boil and thicken, then remove from heat and set aside.

▶ Steam parsnip until soft and then mash. Add half the gravy and combine well.

▶ Drain chickpeas and puree with the other half of the gravy until smooth. Add chickpea mixture to parsnip mixture and mix until well combined.

Bean and Tomato Puree

This is a quick and easy recipe that you can whip up in minutes and pour over your baby's vegies. It's an excellent source of iron and protein.

300 g tin red kidney beans

1 tablespoon tomato paste

► Don't drain beans. Combine beans with tomato paste and puree or mash.

NOTE: for older children leave the beans whole.

Lentil Puree

This is another dish that is high in iron and protein, and can be poured over vegies.

½ cup red or brown lentils

1 tablespoon Massel gravy powder

► Cook lentils in boiling water until tender, drain and place in bowl.

► Place 1 cup of water in a small saucepan on medium heat and add gravy powder. Whisk mixture until well combined, allow to boil and thicken, then remove from heat. Add enough gravy to the lentils to make a sloppy consistency. Depending on what type of lentils you use (red lentils are usually split, and brown lentils are whole), you can leave the mixture as is or puree.

CUSTARDS AND YOGHURTS

Fruit Topping

Cottage Cheese Whip

Mango and Tofu Cream

Strawberry and Tofu Cream

Apricot and Tofu Cream

Custard

Eggless Custard

When your baby is **6 months** old, you can start to introduce yoghurt, custard and cheese to their diet.

The ideal yoghurt to buy is plain yoghurt, as the flavoured ones tend to be very sweet. There are now soy yoghurts on the market if you choose to feed your baby a vegan diet or if your child has allergies or intolerances to dairy products. Fruit toppings can be made to go with the yoghurt, or you could serve yoghurt with stewed fruit or with fresh, ripe pureed fruit.

Fruit Toppings

425 g tin unsweetened peaches, pears, apricots, pineapple or fruit
  salad

► Drain contents of tin, puree and store in fridge for up to 3 days.
  Add a couple of tablespoons of fruit topping to yoghurt to serve.

Cottage Cheese Whip

Here is a yummy alternative to yoghurt.

440 g tin unsweetened fruit salad or 1 cup chopped fresh fruit salad

250 g cottage cheese

► Drain tin of fruit salad well, otherwise the whip will be too runny.
  Add the drained tin of fruit salad or fresh fruit salad to the
  cottage cheese and blend until smooth.

The whip will thicken once chilled in the refrigerator. It can be
stored in the fridge for up to 3 days. Serve it on its own or with
some fruit.

Mango and Tofu Cream

This recipe is great for those babies who can't have dairy products because of allergies or for the vegan baby. Tofu is a great source of iron.

1 medium-sized mango

300 g silken tofu

➤ Remove skin and seed from mango. Combine mango flesh and silken tofu and blend until smooth and creamy.

Store in fridge for 2–3 days.

Strawberry and Tofu Cream

1½ cups strawberries

300 g silken tofu

➤ Combine strawberries and silken tofu and blend until smooth and creamy. If the strawberries are a bit tart, add a generous teaspoon of berry jam to the mixture before blending or use a teaspoon of honey if your baby is over 12 months old.

Store in fridge for 2–3 days.

Apricot and Tofu Cream

425 g tin apricot halves in natural juice

300 g silken tofu

➤ Drain apricots, combine with tofu and blend until smooth and creamy. An optional extra is a generous teaspoon of apricot jam added to the mixture while blending, or a teaspoon of honey if your baby is over 12 months old.

Store in fridge for 2–3 days.

Custard

The way to make custard if you are pressed for time is to use packet varieties.

Follow the instructions on the back of the packet using ordinary milk or soy milk. To make the custard a bit thicker, just add a little bit of extra custard powder. Thick custard is easier to feed to your baby than runny custard.

You could add a couple of drops of vanilla essence or a sprinkle of cinnamon or, to make banana custard, add a mashed banana during the cooking process.

For those of you who don't want to use the packet custard, here is another option.

Eggless custard

2 cups milk or vanilla flavoured soy milk

2 tablespoons cornflour

► Place all but ¼ cup of milk in a small saucepan on medium heat and bring to the boil. Mix cornflour in a separate dish with the remaining milk until cornflour is well combined. Add cornflour mixture to saucepan and whisk, making sure no lumps form. Whisk continually until custard has thickened and remove pan from heat.

If you use cow's milk, add a few drops of vanilla essence and a tablespoon of sugar as the vanilla soy milk has some sugar in it. Eggless custard stores in the fridge for 3 days.

SNACK, LUNCH AND SANDWICH-FILLING IDEAS

Snacks

Snacks can be given at morning and afternoon tea times. You should try to discourage snacking at any other time of the day or you may find your child won't eat their main meals. Constant snacking can encourage poor eating patterns.

Morning and afternoon tea provide energy for your child's busy day. When to introduce your child to morning and afternoon tea depends on the individual baby or child and their needs.

The times below are a guideline only. Obviously, the more sleep your baby or child has in the day, the harder it is to fit in a morning or afternoon tea. As your child becomes older and sleeps less in the day, morning and afternoon tea become more significant. Also, be careful not to give morning or afternoon tea too close to the main meals. Usually a juice will be enough to tide them over if it's getting too close to lunch or dinner.

Here is a sample meal plan:

7–8 am	Breakfast
10 am	Morning tea
12–1 pm	Lunch
3 pm	Afternoon tea
5–6 pm	Dinner

Try to avoid sweet snacks such as cakes and biscuits as this will only give your child a sweet tooth and it will make it harder for you when you want to give them something healthy like a piece of fruit. Here are some morning and afternoon tea ideas to be offered with a juice or a drink to babies aged **8–12 months**. Try and provide foods that promote finger-food eating.

Rusk

Soft cheese stick or soft cheese slice

Half to a whole banana

Grated hard cheese

Grated apple, carrot or celery

Ripe, soft, fruit pieces (for example, rockmelon, banana, watermelon, kiwi fruit, pear)

Large dried apricots or pears

Plain biscuit (for example, arrowroot)

Half a sandwich

For toddlers aged **12 months–2 years**, choose from the babies' options, and the following:

Fresh fruit cut into pieces (for example, apple and orange)

Rice cake or savoury biscuit with tahini, nut paste, vegemite or avocado

For children aged **2 years** and over, add the following to your morning and afternoon tea choices:

Any fruit

Any dried fruit (for example, sultanas, dates, figs, apple)

Savoury biscuit and cheese

Weetbix or Vitabrit with a spread

Muesli bar

Celery sticks stuffed with peanut butter or cottage cheese

Carrot or cheese sticks with some dip (for example, mashed avocado)

For the summer months add:

Frozen watermelon pieces

Ice blocks made from fresh fruit juice (you can buy special icy pole makers to do this)

A frozen banana on an ice block stick (for a special treat, you could dip the banana in melted carob before freezing)

Lunch ideas

The following dishes can be prepared for lunch, or as a quick and easy alternative at tea time for babies aged **6–12 months**:

Sandwiches. Refer to sandwich filling ideas on page 74

Fruit with yoghurt or custard (refer to yoghurt and custard section on page 67)

Toast soldiers and baked beans (it's a good idea to mash the beans when introducing them for the first time)

Toast soldiers and spaghetti (chop spaghetti into small pieces when introducing it for the first time)

Both baked beans and spaghetti are available in 130 g tins, which make perfect portions.

Mashed avocado and yoghurt

Mashed avocado with cottage cheese

Scrambled eggs (for babies aged 6–9 months, make scrambled eggs with the yolk only; for babies aged 9 months and over, use the whole egg)

For babies aged **12 months** and over choose from the options for younger babies or the following:

Fried or poached egg on toast

2-minute noodles with or without the seasonings

Vegetarian chicken nuggets (you can buy these in the frozen-food section of the supermarket)

Oven-baked potato wedges served with mashed avocado

Vegetarian hot dogs served on its own with tomato sauce or for the older child, 3 years and over, serve in a hot dog roll (these hot dogs can be bought in the refrigerated section of the supermarket.)

Sandwich-filling ideas

Sandwiches, if served with healthy fillings, can provide a nutritious meal for your baby or child. Here are some sandwich-filling ideas for babies aged **6–12 months** to get you started:

Vegemite or marmite

Mashed avocado

Tahini (a paste made out of pureed sesame seeds, with a slightly nutty taste. You can buy it in the health food section of the supermarket.)

Mashed banana

Cheese spread

Grated cheese

Cottage cheese with grated apple

Cream cheese, blended with cucumber

Vegetarian luncheon roll, sliced thinly

Here are some more ideas for children aged **12 months** and over:

Peanut butter and other nut butters such as cashew, almond and
macadamia (these can be purchased in the health food section of
the supermarket)

Nut paste with honey (cashew nut butter and honey is very
scrummy!)

Mashed banana and honey

Mashed hard-boiled egg with a little mayonnaise or yoghurt with
fresh chives or parsley

Baked beans

Tahini and honey

Mashed avocado with grated carrot and cheese

Mashed avocado with grated carrot and sliced tomato

Vegetarian luncheon roll with tomato sauce

Hummus with sliced tomato and lettuce

Again, these ideas are only to get you started. The combinations
are limitless!

When first introducing sandwiches to your baby at the age of
6 months, use a soft brown bread and later, as your child gets
older and more competent at sandwich eating, you can increase
the bulkiness of the bread. Also, start off with a fairly basic filling
such as vegemite or tahini and work up to more complex fillings.

For children aged **3 years** and over, start offering different
types of breads, for example, rolls, bagels, focaccia, Turkish
bread, pita pockets and lavash bread. The options regarding what
type of bread to use are as broad as the options regarding fillings.

At this age they will also enjoy eating toasted sandwiches and open melts.

Most breads can be frozen so you can keep bulk amounts in the freezer.

Send **school-aged** children off to school with pita pockets with fillings or roll some fillings up with lavash bread to make lunches more fun.

In the pasta section of your supermarket you can now buy concentrated spreads that can be used as a base for sandwich fillings. These are pesto, sun-dried tomato, roasted capsicum and roasted vegetable spreads. (Check the labels on these spreads before you buy as some companies put chicken bouillon in them.)

These spreads in conjunction with salad ingredients such as mashed avocado, hummus or cheese, can be made into colourful, tasty sandwiches.

Here are some yummy combinations for **school-aged** children:

Bagel with pesto spread with mashed avocado and salad

Sandwich with sun-dried tomato spread with sliced vegetarian luncheon roll on its own or with salad

Pocket pita bread with hummus and tabouli

Sandwich with roasted vegetable spread with cheese and salad

Lavash bread rolled up with hummus, sun-dried capsicum spread and salad

Focaccia with mashed avocado and salad

Hummus

You can buy hummus at your local supermarket or gourmet delicatessen but if you want to make your own, here is a recipe. It's quick and easy and has a storage life in the fridge of approximately 2 weeks. It can be used as a spread on anything. Hummus being made from chickpeas has a good iron, protein, calcium and zinc content.

2 x 300 g tins chickpeas

2–3 cloves peeled garlic

1 teaspoon salt

juice of 2 lemons

¾ cup tahini

¼ cup chopped parsley

¼ cup chopped spring onions

shake of black and cayenne pepper (optional)

➤ Drain chickpeas and put all ingredients in the blender. Blend until well combined and smooth.

Store hummus in fridge in an airtight container.

NOTE: If you want to use hummus as a dip, add some water while blending for a softer consistency.

# JUICES

When your baby is about **6 months** old you can start offering some half-strength juice, either commercially bought or freshly squeezed. If you are using commercially bought juice choose juice with no added sugar. If your baby has had problems with constipation, you may have offered them some diluted prune juice before they were 6 months old (refer to stewed fruit and cooked vegies section on page 58). Juice is an addition to your baby's diet, it is not a substitute for breast milk or formula feed.

Obtain a cup with a good spout. Some bottles come with spout attachments—these are okay. Having handles on the cup is a good idea so your child can learn to hold it themselves. If you wish to introduce a straw instead of a spout you can do this but it may take your baby a little more time to master. Make sure you clean the straw attachment well as it is an easy trap for germs.

The best time to offer half-strength juice is at morning and afternoon tea time. Start with something alkaline such as apple or pear juice which is gentle on the digestive system, and work up to the more acidic juices, such as orange or blackcurrant juice. It's a good idea to offer the same juice for a week or so, so you can watch for any allergic reactions, before trying a new one. Always offer half-strength juice (for example, 30 ml cooled boiled water with 30 ml juice). Once babies are over **12 months** old their digestive systems are more mature and able to take full-strength juice. If your baby is under 12 months, you should boil the water before giving it to your baby. Keep a jug of boiled water in the fridge and replace with a fresh batch every 24 hours.

When you first offer juice to your baby, you will need to hold the cup for them until they learn to hold the cup themselves. They may not like the taste of juice, or they may cough, splutter or cry from the new experience. All this is normal, so don't worry. Just try again later or the next day. Some babies will master juice drinking quite quickly—within a couple of days. Others may take a couple of weeks to get the hang of it. Don't give up too soon!

As your baby gets older and more used to the spout, you can start offering juice without the spout attachment.

Juice is a great thing to have in your bag when you are out, especially if your baby starts to get hungry and you can't drop everything for a feed (for example, when you are standing in a supermarket queue). On a hot day, carry some extra juice in your bag as your baby can get very thirsty. It's a good idea to offer cooled boiled water on its own on a regular basis so your baby doesn't become dependent on juice only.

FOR BABIES AGED 8–12 MONTHS

Spinach and Tomato Risotto

Rice and Vegetable Patties

Sweet Potato Patties

Rice and Potato Balls

Pasta with Spinach Sauce

Pasta with Vegetable Cheese Sauce

Pasta with Lentil Tomato Sauce

Ratatouille

Baked Tofu Cubes

I've kept the seasonings of these recipes to a minimum so, to the adult palate, they may taste a touch on the bland side. Once your baby is **12 months** old, you can use these recipes but jazz them up with more seasonings, as your baby's digestive system is more mature and able to take more-flavoured food. Introduce these dishes slowly into your baby's diet along with their usual vegies.

Spinach and Tomato Risotto

¾ cup uncooked brown rice (short or long grain or rice of choice)

butter or olive oil

2 spring onions, chopped

2 tomatoes, peeled and chopped (refer to page 65)

1 cup chopped baby or English spinach

sprinkle organic herb salt (optional)

➤ Cook rice in boiling water until tender, drain and set aside.

➤ In a small saucepan fry spring onions on medium heat in a little butter or olive oil till spring onions are lightly browned. Add tomatoes. You may need to add a little water (about ¼ cup) at this stage to prevent mixture sticking on bottom of saucepan. Simmer mixture gently for a few minutes, then add spinach and simmer until spinach is wilted. Add a sprinkle of herb salt.

➤ Take pan off heat and allow mixture to cool a little, then lightly blend, but do not puree. Add cooked rice to tomato mixture, and return saucepan to heat. Over low heat, stir rice and tomato mixture together until well combined.

Makes approximately 6 small meals. This dish can be frozen.

Rice and Vegetable Patties

⅓ cup uncooked brown rice or rice of choice

butter or olive oil

2 spring onions, chopped

1 medium carrot, grated

1 medium zucchini, grated

130 g tin creamed corn

¼ cup breadcrumbs

2 tablespoons tahini

handful freshly chopped parsley

sprinkle of organic herb salt (optional)

approximately 1 cup extra breadcrumbs for crumbing

extra olive oil for frying (optional)

➤ Cook rice in boiling water until tender, drain and set aside.

➤ In a small saucepan lightly fry spring onions until soft in a little butter or olive oil. Allow to cool.

➤ Combine cooked rice and spring onions in a large bowl, and add carrot, zucchini, creamed corn, breadcrumbs, tahini, parsley and a sprinkle of herb salt.

➤ Mix well, cover and place in fridge until mixture firms up. (Usually I prepare mixture in the morning and in the afternoon mould the patties ready for frying.)

➤ When mixture is firm, shape into small patties and roll in breadcrumbs. Cook patties on medium heat in a little olive oil in a non-stick frypan until golden on both sides. Drain on absorbent paper.

Makes approximately 16 small patties, which can be frozen.

Sweet Potato Patties

1 medium-sized sweet potato, peeled and sliced

butter or olive oil

2 spring onions, chopped

1 medium zucchini, grated

1 medium carrot, grated

handful chopped fresh parsley

¼ cup sesame seeds

½ cup wheatgerm

1 cup breadcrumbs

organic herb salt (optional)

approximately 1 cup extra breadcrumbs for crumbing

extra olive oil for frying (optional)

➤ Steam sweet potato until soft, mash and set aside.

➤ Saute spring onions in a saucepan on medium heat in a little butter or olive oil until lightly browned.

➤ Combine sweet potato and spring onions with other ingredients in a large bowl and mix well.

➤ Cover and place in the fridge for a couple of hours to allow patty mixture to firm up. Once mixture is firm, form small patties, and roll in breadcrumbs.

➤ Fry patties in a little olive oil in a non-stick frypan until golden brown on both sides.

Makes approximately 22 small patties, which can be frozen.

Rice and Potato Balls

⅓ cup uncooked brown rice or rice of choice

butter or olive oil

2 spring onions, chopped

2 medium-sized potatoes, cooked and mashed

1 cup cooked, finely chopped broccoli

¼ cup wheatgerm

sprinkle of organic herb salt (optional)

approximately ½ cup sesame seeds

approximately ½ cup breadcrumbs

extra olive oil, for frying

➤ Cook rice in boiling water until soft, drain and set aside.

➤ Pan fry spring onions in a little butter or olive oil until soft. Allow to cool a little.

➤ Combine cooked rice and spring onions in a bowl, adding mashed potato, broccoli, wheatgerm and herb salt. Mix until well combined. Cover and place in fridge until mixture is firm. (This usually takes a few hours.) Once mixture has firmed up, roll into small balls and roll in a mixture of sesame seeds and breadcrumbs.

➤ Fry balls in olive oil until golden brown. (I found frying the balls easiest in a wok.) Drain balls on absorbent paper.

Makes approximately 30 small balls, which can be frozen.

Pasta with Spinach Sauce

1 cup pasta (for example, small shells)

1 tablespoon butter or dairy-free margarine

2 spring onions, chopped

1 tablespoon cornflour

¾ cup milk or soy milk

1 cup chopped baby spinach or English spinach

sprinkle of organic herb salt (optional)

➤ Cook pasta in boiling water until tender. Drain and set aside.

➤ While pasta is cooking, in a small saucepan fry spring onions in butter on medium heat until spring onions are lightly browned.

➤ Remove pan from heat, add flour and mix to a paste. Add milk and whisk until well combined. Return pan to heat and bring milk to the boil, whisking all the time until the mixture thickens. Add spinach and stir until spinach has wilted in the mixture. Add a sprinkle of herb salt. Remove pan from heat and allow mixture to cool a little. Puree.

➤ Divide pasta into five portions and place a couple of spoonfuls of sauce on each serving of pasta.

Makes approximately 5 small meals, and the meals can be frozen.

NOTE: for a slightly different taste add ¼ cup grated cheese to the sauce when adding spinach.

Pasta with Vegetable Cheese Sauce

1 cup pasta (for example, small shells)

1 tablespoon butter or dairy-free margarine

2 spring onions, chopped

1 tablespoon cornflour

¾ cup milk or soy milk

¼ cup grated cheese

1 small carrot, grated

1 small zucchini, grated

130 g tin creamed corn

sprinkle of organic herb salt (optional)

► Cook pasta in boiling water until tender. Drain and set aside.

► While pasta is cooking, in a small saucepan fry spring onions in butter on medium heat until spring onions are lightly browned.

► Remove pan from heat, add cornflour and mix to a paste. Add milk and whisk until well combined. Return pan to heat and allow milk to boil and thicken, whisking all the time. Add grated cheese, carrot, zucchini and creamed corn, and mix until well combined. Stir mixture for a couple of minutes until carrot and zucchini soften. Remove pan from heat and add a sprinkle of herb salt. Allow mixture to cool a little, then lightly blend but do not puree.

► Divide pasta into small meal sizes. This recipe makes approximately 5 baby servings. Place a couple of spoonfuls of sauce onto each serving of pasta. These meals can be frozen.

NOTE: you can make this dish without the cheese.

Pasta with Lentil Tomato Sauce

¼ cup red, green or brown lentils

2 spring onions, chopped

1 stick celery, finely sliced

olive oil

1 x 400 g tin tomatoes

1 tablespoon tomato paste

handful chopped fresh parsley or basil

sprinkle of organic herb salt (optional)

1 cup pasta (for example, small shells)

► Cook lentils in boiling water until tender. Drain and set aside.

► While pasta is cooking, fry spring onions and celery in a saucepan on medium heat with a little olive oil until soft. Puree tomatoes and add to saucepan. Reduce heat and gently simmer. Add tomato paste, cooked lentils, herbs and organic herb salt to pan and simmer gently for approximately 10 minutes. Remove pan from heat.

► Cook pasta in boiling water until tender, drain, and divide into small meals. Pour sauce over pasta.

Makes approximately 5 small meals, which can be frozen.

Ratatouille

olive oil

1 small onion, chopped

1 medium-sized eggplant, diced

1 medium zucchini, diced

1 small red or green capsicum, diced

1 cup tomato juice

3 tomatoes, peeled and chopped (refer to page 65)

handful fresh basil, chopped

1 clove garlic, crushed (optional)

sprinkle of organic herb salt (optional)

➤ In a large saucepan on medium heat fry onion and eggplant in some olive oil until the onion is transparent. Add zucchini and capsicum, and cook for a further few minutes.

➤ Add tomato juice, tomatoes, basil, garlic and herb salt, and simmer for approximately 30 minutes until ingredients are soft. Blend mixture lightly but do not completely puree.

➤ Serve ratatouille on its own or with rice, pasta or couscous.

Makes approximately 8 small meals, which can be frozen.

Baked Tofu Cubes

Tofu is a great source of iron and protein. Here is a fun way of introducing it to your baby. Cut the cubes the right size for your baby to pick up with their fingers, so they can feed themselves.

olive oil

firm tofu cut into cubes (5 cubes of tofu is a suitable serving for your baby)

jar of plain tomato pasta sauce (check jar for ingredients, you don't want it too spicy)

➤ Brush a small baking dish with olive oil, place cubes of tofu in dish and brush tofu lightly with olive oil. Bake at 200°C for 20 minutes or until tofu is lightly browned. Drain tofu on absorbent paper.

Serve tofu cubes with a small amount of pasta sauce. Makes 1 serving.

Tofu cubes are unsuitable for freezing, but will store in the fridge for 1–2 days.

FOR TODDLERS AGED OVER 1 AND UNDER 4

Fried Rice

Tomato and Capsicum Risotto

Bronnie's Rice Patties

Cottage Cheese Patties

Corn and Zucchini Fritters

Spinach Pikelets

Pumpkin Pancakes

Vegetarian Spaghetti Bolognese

Pasta with Tomato and Basil Sauce

Vegetable and Pasta Bake

Eggplant Bake

Baked Bean Pie

Lentil Casserole

Mini Pizzas

Sausage Rolls

Tofu Bites

Vegetable and Noodle Stir Fry

Tofu with Vegetables

One of the great benefits of vegetarian cooking is that the recipes can be modified slightly to suit your own family's needs, without turning them into a flop! The recipes in this section can be given to your baby in conjunction with the recipes from the previous section, designed for babies aged 8–12 months. Now your child has reached the age of 1 year, you can jazz up those recipes with your own favourite herbs and seasonings.

At the age of 12 months, your child can basically eat what you eat, so most of the following recipes are in family-sized meals. You can continue cooking separately for your toddler and dividing these recipes into smaller meals and freezing them, or you can cook these dishes for the whole family, adapting them to suit your needs as some of these recipes are more child orientated.

If the recipe indicates it serves 4 adults, you will get approximately 8–10 small servings out of it. As the age group in this section is fairly broad, keep your baby/child's age in mind when preparing the recipes. Cut vegetables into small pieces when your child is young. An older child can cope with a variety of sizes.

Fried Rice

1 250 g packet fresh bean sprouts

3 spring onions, chopped

oil

variety of vegetables of choice, chopped or sliced depending on what your baby or child can manage, for example:

2 sticks celery, sliced

1 medium carrot, sliced

1 small red capsicum, diced

6 button mushrooms, sliced

2 cups uncooked brown long grain rice or rice of choice

soy sauce to taste

herb salt

2 eggs, beaten (optional)

► In a wok or large electric fry pan on medium heat, place bean sprouts and chopped spring onions in a little oil and cook until soft. Add vegetables and stir fry until tender. Turn heat right down and leave for the moment.

► Cook rice in boiling water until tender but not too soft. Drain rice, rinse with hot water and drain again. Add cooked rice to vegetables and stir gently until vegies and rice are well combined. Add soy sauce and herb salt to your taste.

► While rice is cooking, make the omelette. Place eggs in a frying pan and cook until lightly browned on both sides. Remove omelette from pan, roll up and slice thinly. Add omelette to fried rice just before serving.

Serves 4 adults, and can be frozen.

Tomato and Capsicum Risotto

1 ½ cups uncooked brown short or long grain rice or rice of choice

25 g butter or dairy-free margarine

3 tablespoons olive oil

1 onion, chopped

1 red or green capsicum, diced

4 tomatoes, peeled (see page 65)

1 clove garlic, crushed

handful fresh basil

handful fresh parsley

herb salt to taste

➤ Cook rice until tender, drain and set aside.

➤ Melt butter with oil in a large saucepan. Add onion and capsicum to pan and cook until onion is transparent. Chop tomatoes and add to the saucepan along with garlic, herbs and salt. Simmer mixture for approximately 10 minutes or until tomatoes are soft.

➤ Add rice and stir until mixture is well combined and rice is heated through.

Serves 3 adults, and can be frozen.

Bronnie's Rice Patties

1 x 30 g packet spring vegetable soup mix

1 onion, finely chopped

2 tablespoons self-raising flour

½ cup breadcrumbs

½ cup chopped fresh herbs (for example, chives, parsley and sage)

sprinkle of organic herb salt

½ cup uncooked brown rice or rice of choice

1 cup grated mozzarella cheese

1 egg, beaten (optional)

approximately 1 cup extra breadcrumbs for crumbing

olive oil for frying (optional)

➤ Place soup mix, onion, flour, breadcrumbs, fresh herbs and herb salt in a bowl and combine well.

➤ Cook rice in boiling water until soft, drain well, then add to other ingredients in bowl. Add mozzarella cheese at the same time as rice—the warmth from the cooked rice will melt the cheese. Then add the beaten egg. If mixture is a bit wet at this stage you can add some extra breadcrumbs to firm it up, or you can put it in the fridge for a couple of hours, as this will firm mixture as well. Form mixture into patties and coat patties with breadcrumbs. Fry patties in a non-stick frying pan in a little olive oil on medium heat until golden.

Makes approximately 20 patties, which can be frozen.

Cottage Cheese Patties

¾ cup rolled oats

½ cup walnuts

1 ¼ cups breadcrumbs

1 onion, finely chopped

500 g cottage cheese

1 egg (optional)

½ cup chopped fresh parsley

sprinkle of lemon pepper

sprinkle of organic herb salt

extra breadcrumbs for crumbing

olive oil for frying (optional)

► Place rolled oats and walnuts in food processor and blend until mixture resembles fine breadcrumbs. Transfer to bowl and add all other ingredients. Combine well.

► At this stage you can put mixture in the fridge for a couple of hours if not ready to make patties straightaway. The mixture will become more firm in the fridge. Form mixture into small patties and coat patties with breadcrumbs. Fry patties in frying pan on medium heat with a little olive oil until golden.

Makes approximately 20 patties, which can be frozen.

Corn and Zucchini Fritters

310 g tin creamed corn

130 g tin corn kernels

1 medium zucchini, grated

1 cup milk or soy milk

60 g butter or dairy-free margarine, melted

2 eggs, beaten

1 ¼ cups plain flour

2 teaspoons baking powder

herb salt to taste

➤ Combine creamed corn, corn kernels, zucchini, milk, butter and eggs in a medium-sized bowl. Mix well. Add flour, baking powder and salt, and stir until well combined.

➤ Usually 1–2 spoonfuls is ideal for a child-size fritter. Place spoonfuls of mixture in a non-stick frypan and cook until bubbles start to rise on the first side. Turn fritter over and cook until golden brown.

Makes approximately 26 fritters, which can be frozen.

Spinach Pikelets

1 ½ cups wholemeal self-raising flour

2 eggs

1 ¼ cups milk or soy milk

½ bunch spinach, or 5 large leaves, washed and chopped

3 spring onions, finely chopped

handful fresh chives, chopped

sprinkle of herb salt

➤ Blend flour, eggs, milk and spinach in a food processor until smooth, and transfer to a bowl.

➤ Add spring onions, chives and herb salt to mixture and mix well.

➤ Cook spoonfuls of mixture on medium heat in a non-stick frying pan. Usually 1–2 large spoonfuls is enough for a child-size pikelet. When bubbles rise on the first side turn pikelets over. Cook pikelets until golden on both sides.

Serve pikelets by themselves or with a mild tomato salsa, or spread them with a little butter or hummus.
Makes approximately 25 pikelets, which can be frozen.

Pumpkin Pancakes

250 g pumpkin, cooked

250 g potato, cooked

30 g butter or dairy-free margarine

2 tablespoons plain flour

2 tablespoons self-raising flour

1 egg

2–3 spring onions, finely chopped

sprinkle of herb salt

sprinkle of nutmeg

➤ Place cooked pumpkin and potato in a food processor with butter and blend until smooth. Transfer mixture to a bowl and add rest of ingredients. Combine well.

➤ Cook spoonfuls of mixture on medium heat in a non-stick frypan. Usually 1–2 large spoonfuls is enough for a child-size pancake. When bubbles start to rise on the first side turn pancake over. Cook pancakes until golden on both sides.

Serve pancakes by themselves or with a little butter or mild salsa. Makes approximately 15 small pancakes, which can be frozen.

Vegetarian Spaghetti Bolognese

olive oil

1 onion, chopped

2 x 400 g tins tomatoes

2 tablespoons tomato paste

handful each chopped fresh parsley and basil

2 sprigs fresh oregano

herb salt to taste

1 x 125 g packet of 'Realeat' vegie burger mix

2 cloves garlic, crushed

➤ Fry onion in a little olive oil in a large saucepan on medium heat until onion is transparent. Puree tomatoes and add to onion. Add tomato paste, fresh herbs and salt to pan and combine well. Stir in vegie burger mix. You will need to add some extra water at this stage as the burger mix absorbs a lot of liquid. Add enough water, ¼ cup at a time, until you get the consistency you desire. Add garlic and allow sauce to simmer on low heat for 10–15 minutes. Stir occasionally to prevent sticking.

Serve sauce over your child's favourite pasta.
Serves 4–6 adults, and can be frozen.

Pasta with Tomato and Basil Sauce

olive oil

1 small onion, chopped

400 g tin tomatoes or 5–6 fresh tomatoes, peeled and chopped

1 tablespoon tomato paste

herb salt to taste

1–2 cloves garlic, crushed

handful each fresh basil and parsley, chopped

2 sprigs of fresh oregano, chopped

➤ Fry onion in a little olive oil in a saucepan on medium heat until onion is transparent. Add tomatoes, tomato paste and salt to taste. If you are using tinned tomatoes, add ⅓ cup of water. If you are using fresh tomatoes, add ½ cup water. Simmer sauce over low heat for 10–15 minutes. You can leave the sauce chunky or you can puree it. Add garlic and herbs, and simmer for a further 5 minutes. Remove pan from heat and serve sauce with your child's favourite pasta.

Serves 4 adults, and can be frozen.

Vegetable and Pasta Bake

500 g pasta (for example, spirals or shells)

olive oil

variety of vegetables of choice, chopped or sliced depending on what your baby or child can manage, for example:

> 6 button mushrooms
>
> small floret of broccoli
>
> 2 zucchini
>
> 2 finger eggplants
>
> 6 baby yellow squash
>
> 3–4 spring onions

2 cloves garlic, crushed

herb salt to taste

handful chopped fresh parsley

handful chopped fresh basil

500 g your favourite tomato pasta sauce

approximately 1½ cups grated mozzarella cheese

➤ Cook pasta in boiling water until tender but not too soft. Drain and set aside.

➤ While pasta is cooking, chop vegies and stir fry on medium heat in olive oil with garlic, salt and fresh herbs in large electric frying pan or wok until tender. Gently combine cooked pasta with vegetables. Place mixture in a large baking dish and pour tomato sauce over the top. Spread mozzarella cheese to desired thickness, evenly over vegetable and pasta bake.

➤ Bake in moderate oven approximately 15–20 minutes or until cheese is melted and golden brown.

Serves 6 adults, and can be frozen.

Eggplant Bake

olive oil

1 onion, chopped

2 x 400 g tins tomatoes

2 tablespoons tomato paste

handful each chopped fresh basil and parsley

2 sprigs fresh oregano, chopped

2 cloves garlic, crushed

herb salt

2 large eggplants, sliced thinly

approximately 1½ cups grated mozzarella cheese

► Fry onion in a large saucepan in a little olive oil on medium heat until onion is transparent. Puree tomatoes and add to onion. Add tomato paste, fresh herbs, garlic and salt to taste to pan. Combine ingredients well, reduce heat and allow to simmer for 10–15 minutes.

► Remove pan from heat.

► Lay out eggplant slices on baking trays. Brush one side lightly with olive oil and place tray under grill on medium to high heat. When first side is lightly browned, turn eggplant over with tongs. Brush other side with olive oil, place tray back under grill and cook until eggplant is light brown and soft.

► Place a thin layer of tomato sauce over bottom of a large baking dish (for example a lasagna dish), and place a layer of grilled eggplant on top. Repeat process two more times, and top with remaining tomato sauce and grated mozzarella cheese. Bake in a moderate oven for approximately 20 minutes until cheese is golden brown and bubbling.

Serve 4–6 adults with a side dish of pasta or rice, and can be frozen.

Baked Bean Pie

680 g tin baked beans

1 medium zucchini, grated

3 medium-sized potatoes, peeled and chopped

¼ cup milk or soy milk

herb salt

handful fresh chives, chopped (optional)

➤ Place baked beans in a medium-sized ovenproof dish. Add grated zucchini and combine gently.

➤ Steam potatoes until soft. Mash potatoes with milk and herb salt to taste until potatoes are desired consistency. You may need to add more milk. Fold chopped chives through mashed potato, then spread mashed potato evenly over baked beans.

➤ Place dish in preheated 180°C oven and bake for 20 minutes. Finish off pie under the grill for a few minutes to allow the top to go brown and crispy.

A fun way to serve baked bean pie to your child is to bake pies in individual child-sized baking dishes.
Serves 4 adults, and can be frozen.

Lentil Casserole

oil

1 leek, chopped

900 ml water

350 g green or brown lentils

1 vegetable style Massel Ultracube

3 tablespoons tomato paste

1 clove garlic, crushed

handful fresh parsley, chopped

herb salt

3 celery sticks, finely sliced

3 tomatoes, diced

➤ In a large saucepan fry leek in a little oil until leek is soft. Add water, lentils, stock cube, tomato paste, garlic, parsley and herb salt to taste. Bring to boil, then allow to simmer for about 25 minutes, stirring occasionally. Add celery and tomatoes to pan. Allow mixture to simmer for a further 25–30 minutes or until lentils are tender. If lentils get a little dry, add some more water.

Lentils can be served over couscous, rice or pasta, or place lentils in a baking dish, top with mashed potato and pop under the grill to brown the top.
Serves 4 adults, and can be frozen.

Mini Pizzas

1 x 400 g packet wholemeal English muffins

1 x 140 g jar sun-dried tomato pesto (you will probably only use half
the jar)

approximately 2 cups grated mozzarella cheese

1 packet of Longalife 'not pepperoni', sliced into strips

1 red capsicum, sliced

approximately 10 button mushrooms, sliced

1 baby eggplant, cut into thin slices

➤ Halve muffins and lay out halves on a baking tray. Spread muffins
with tomato pesto. Sprinkle a layer of mozzarella cheese over the
pesto, then place on top of cheese some 'not pepperoni', capsicum,
mushrooms and, lastly, top with a slice of eggplant. Finish off with
another sprinkle of grated mozzarella cheese.

➤ Cook pizzas in a preheated 200°C oven for 10 minutes or until
cheese is brown and bubbly.

Make as few or as many pizzas as you want to, and the pizzas can
be frozen.

NOTE: You can experiment with different toppings until you find a
combination that is a favourite with your child. For example:

    basil pesto instead of sun-dried tomato pesto

    zucchini

    sun-dried tomatoes or fresh tomato, sliced

    pineapple

    baby corn

    spinach or broccoli

    bocconcini cheese, sliced, instead of grated mozzarella cheese

Sausage Rolls

1 cup cottage cheese

½ cup or 50 g packet of pecans

3 eggs

1 stick celery, chopped

1 onion, chopped

1 tablespoon soy sauce

½ cup dried breadcrumbs

1 cup rolled oats

herb salt

couple of handfuls fresh herbs, for example, parsley, chives, sage and
    rosemary, finely chopped

3 sheets puff pastry

extra milk for brushing sausage rolls

sesame seeds to sprinkle on top of sausage rolls

➤ Place cottage cheese, pecans, eggs, celery, onion and soy sauce in a
food processor and blend until smooth. Transfer mixture to a
mixing bowl and add breadcrumbs, rolled oats, herb salt and fresh
herbs. Stir until well combined. Mixture may be a little sloppy but
if you set it aside for 10 minutes or so it will thicken up, as the
rolled oats will absorb the liquid. If it is still sloppy after 10
minutes, you could add some extra breadcrumbs. Also, an hour or
so in the fridge will make the mixture a little firmer.

➤ Cut each sheet of puff pastry in half, to give you 6 pieces. Spoon
mixture evenly along one side of the piece of pastry and roll up.
Milk brushed along the other side will help make the pastry stick
when rolled up. Now cut the roll into 4 even pieces.

▶ Brush with milk and sprinkle with sesame seeds. Repeat process with remaining 5 pieces of puff pastry. Place sausage rolls on baking trays and cook for 20 minutes or until golden brown in a preheated 200°C oven.

Makes 24 sausage rolls, which are suitable for freezing.

Tofu Bites

1 tablespoon honey

2 tablespoons olive oil

1 teaspoon grated ginger

1 clove garlic, crushed

2 teaspoons sesame seeds

250–300 g firm tofu, cut into cubes

▶ Place honey, olive oil, ginger, garlic and sesame seeds in a small bowl and mix together.

▶ Place tofu cubes in a large bowl and pour honey and oil mix over the top. You will need to use your fingers to gently coat the tofu. The tofu breaks very easily, so don't use a spoon. Place tofu bites on a baking tray and spoon over any leftover mixture.

▶ Bake tofu bites in a moderate oven for approximately 15 minutes or until tofu is golden.

Serve with your child's favourite salad or vegies.
This will give you 2–3 child servings.
Unsuitable for freezing. Can be stored in the fridge for 1–2 days.

Vegetable and Noodle Stir Fry

The wonderful thing about stir fries is that you can adapt them to suit your family's likes and needs. You can experiment with different combinations of vegetables, noodles and rice until you find the one that becomes the favourite. The following recipe gives you a start. If you want to increase the number of servings, just add more vegetables! If you want to make a stir fry just for your child or children and not for the adults, reduce the amount of vegetables. When you first introduce stir fries to your child, start off fairly simply, using just a few of their favourite vegies. As they get older, try a larger variety of vegetables.

variety of vegetables of choice cut or sliced into a manageable size for your child, for example:

6 button mushrooms

2 medium zucchini

2–3 spring onions

1 cup fresh green beans, sliced

1 medium-sized floret broccoli

oil

1 clove garlic, crushed

herb salt

600 g fresh noodles or allow 85 g packet of 2-minute noodles per person

➤ Heat your wok or electric frypan to medium heat and pour in a little oil. Add all vegetables except for the broccoli. Stir fry vegetables until just tender, add broccoli, and stir fry for a few more minutes. Add garlic and herb salt to taste, and cooked 2-minute noodles or fresh noodles. Gently combine noodles with vegetables and continue to stir fry until noodles are heated through.

Serves 3 adults, and is unsuitable for freezing.

Tofu with Vegetables

200 g firm smoked tofu, cut into medium-sized cubes

½ cup oil for frying

variety of vegetables of choice cut or sliced into a manageable size for your child, for example:

6 button mushrooms

1 medium zucchini

2–3 spring onions

4 baby yellow squash

medium-sized floret of broccoli

2 stalks celery

½–1 chicken-style Massel Ultracube

1 desertspoon cornflour

1 clove garlic, crushed

herb salt

➤ Heat oil in a wok or electric frypan and fry tofu until it is lightly browned. Remove tofu from wok, drain on absorbent paper and set aside.

➤ Drain most of oil from wok. Place all vegetables, except broccoli, in wok. Stir fry vegetables until just tender, then add chopped broccoli and stir fry for a few more minutes. Mash the ultracube in a small bowl and add ¾ cup cold water. Mix the ultracube and water until well combined, then add cornflour and mix well. Add this mixture to the vegetables and stir fry for a couple of minutes until liquid thickens and coats vegies. Lastly, add fried tofu and garlic and gently combine with the vegetables.

Serve with your favourite rice.
Serves 3 adults, and is unsuitable for freezing.

FOR CHILDREN AGED 4–5 YEARS AND OVER

Vegetarian Lentil Hamburgers

Baked Potatoes

Nat's Nachos

Mexican Tacos

Spinach Pie

Vegetarian Roast with Herb Stuffing

Zucchini Pizza

Sun-dried Tomato Risotto

Pasta with Pesto

Pumpkin Lasagna

Chow Mein

Tofu and Chickpea Stir Fry

Tofu and Vegetables in Peanut Sauce

The recipes in this section are designed for children aged 4 and over but if your 3-year-old is up to the challenge, you can cook these recipes for younger children as well.

Servings for these recipes are in adult sizes. You'll find that the adults won't say no to any of these recipes!

Vegetarian Lentil Hamburgers

1 ½ cups uncooked brown lentils

2 medium-sized potatoes, cooked and mashed

1 ½ cups chopped pumpkin, cooked and mashed

2 stalks celery, finely chopped

1 small onion, finely chopped or grated

½ cup sesame seeds

½ cup almond meal (ground almonds)

herb salt to taste

handful fresh parsley, chopped

handful fresh chives, chopped

► Cook lentils in boiling water until tender. Drain.

► In a large bowl combine cooked lentils, potatoes, pumpkin and rest of ingredients, and mix until well combined. Mould mixture into small burgers and fry burgers in a non-stick frypan until golden on both sides.

Serve in a burger bun with your child's favourite salad ingredients. Makes approximately 20 smallish-sized burgers, which can be frozen.

Baked Potatoes

oil

1 onion, chopped

400 g tin tomatoes

1 tablespoon tomato paste

¼–½ packet of a 35 g packet of chilli con carne seasoning mix
(optional)

½ packet 'Realeat' vegie burger mix

420 g tin red kidney beans, drained

baked potatoes (allow 1 one per person)

avocado, mashed

sour cream

➤ In a saucepan fry onion in a little oil on medium heat until onion
is transparent. Puree tomatoes and add to onion, along with
tomato paste, seasoning and burger mix. Combine well. Add
undrained kidney beans and stir until well combined. Allow
mixture to simmer for a few minutes, then remove from heat.

➤ To bake potatoes, wash potatoes well, then prick all over with a
fork. Wrap each potato in paper towel and cook in the microwave
for approximately 7 minutes. Cooking time will depend on the size
of the potato.

To serve, split baked potato into 4 and top with a couple of spoons
of the bean sauce. Then top with avocado and sour cream.
If offering this dish for the first time to your child, use just a
desertspoon of the seasoning mix.
Makes enough to top approximately 6 potatoes, and bean sauce
can be frozen.

Nat's Nachos

oil

1 onion, chopped

400 g tin tomatoes

1 tablespoon tomato paste

740 g tin red kidney beans, drained

½ x 35 g packet taco seasoning mix

1 large packet (230 g) plain corn chips

approximately 1 ½ cups grated mozzarella cheese

► In a saucepan fry onion with a little oil on medium heat until onion is transparent. Add tomatoes, tomato paste, drained beans and taco seasoning mix. Combine well and allow to simmer on low heat for about 5–10 minutes. Remove pan from heat. At this stage I use my Bamix (upright blender) and blend (not puree) the contents of the saucepan. Pour bean mixture into a 18 x 28 cm baking dish, and top with corn chips. Sprinkle with mozzarella to desired thickness. Place nachos in a moderate oven or under the grill on medium heat until cheese is melted, brown and bubbling.

Serves 3 adults, and the sauce can be frozen. A fun serving suggestion for the children is to make nachos in individual baking dishes or bowls.

NOTE: corn chips are notorious for choking young children. Young children should be supervised when eating meals that contain corn chips, especially if they are trying corn chips for the first time.

Mexican Tacos

oil

1 onion, chopped

3 tomatoes, peeled and chopped (see page 65)

1 medium-sized carrot, grated

1 tablespoon tomato paste

½ x 35 g packet taco seasoning mix

420 g tin red kidney beans, drained

1 x 135 g packet taco shells (12 shells)

SERVING SUGGESTIONS:

diced avocado

diced tomato

shredded lettuce

grated cheese

➤ In a saucepan fry onion on medium heat in a little oil until onion is transparent. Add tomatoes, carrot and ⅓–½ cup water. Allow to simmer for approximately 10 minutes or until tomato and carrot are soft. Add tomato paste, seasoning mix and kidney beans, and simmer for another 10 minutes. Allow excess liquid to evaporate as you don't want the mixture too sloppy. Allow taco filling to cool a little before serving.

➤ Follow instructions on packet of taco shells on how to prepare them. Spoon 1–2 spoonfuls of mixture into shell and top with diced avocado and lettuce, or top with your child's favourite grated cheese and salad mix.

Makes enough to fill 12 taco shells, and taco-filling mixture can be frozen.

Spinach Pie

300 g Australian fetta cheese

3 eggs, beaten

4 spring onions, chopped

sprinkle of pepper

sprinkle of nutmeg

2 large bunches spinach, washed and chopped

60 g butter or soy margarine, melted

12 sheets filo pastry

➤ In a large bowl mash fetta cheese with a fork until crumbly. Add eggs, spring onions, pepper and nutmeg. Mix until well combined.

➤ Add spinach to the bowl. You need to use your hands or a large spoon to combine the spinach with the fetta mixture.

➤ Brush base of a large baking dish or lasagna dish with some of the melted butter. Place 1 sheet of filo pastry in dish and brush lightly with melted butter. Continue with another 5 sheets. Put entire spinach and fetta mix onto your buttered filo sheets and top with the remaining 6 filo sheets, brushing lightly with melted butter in between sheets and on top of uppermost sheet.

➤ Place spinach pie in a preheated moderate oven (180°C) and cook for approximately 35–40 minutes or until filo pastry is golden.

Serves 4–6 adults, and is unsuitable for freezing.

Vegetarian Roast with Herb Stuffing

2 eggs, beaten

1 cup milk or soy milk

½ cup water

1 tablespoon soy sauce

1 teaspoon marmite or vegemite

sprinkle of mixed dried herbs

oil

1 ½ cups gluten flour

Massel gravy powder for sauce

HERB STUFFING

1 onion, finely chopped

handful fresh chives, freshly chopped

3 slices bread

handful fresh parsley

handful fresh sage

handful fresh rosemary

handful fresh thyme

⅓ cup hot water

➤ Make stuffing first. Place onion and chives in a bowl and set aside.

➤ Place 3 slices of bread and rest of herbs in a blender and process until mixture resembles fine crumbs. Add bread mixture to onion mixture and stir until well combined. Add hot water and mix well, mixture should be soft but not too mushy, then set aside.

► In another bowl place eggs, milk, water, soy sauce, marmite and herbs, and beat well with a whisk. Set aside. Do not add gluten flour yet. Preheat a large electric frypan to medium heat. If it's not a non-stick frypan, add a little oil to the bottom and spread it evenly. Now is the time to add gluten flour to the liquid mixture. Add flour a little at a time, whisking continously. As soon as you have whisked the last lot in, quickly pour mixture into your frypan and use a spatula to spread mixture evenly over the bottom. You have to work fast as the gluten flour makes the mixture very thick and it is hard to spread if you take too long. Once mixture is spread over the pan you can breathe a sigh of relief!

► Leave roast to cook on medium heat for approximately 10 minutes or until underside is golden brown.

► By this time the mixture will be quite firm. Turn off the heat. Loosen the roast with a spatula and slide it out onto a bench or a large chopping board. Spread the stuffing onto the uncooked side and roll up roast. You will need some string to keep roll tied up. Usually a tie at each end is sufficient. Place the roast in a deep, long bread tin.

► Make up 500 ml or 2 cups gravy as per instructions, and pour over roast. Cover roast with foil and bake in a moderate oven for 1 hour.

► Remove roast from oven and allow to cool a little before removing roast from tin. Cut string and slice roast.

You can serve roast hot with gravy, or cold—without gravy or with cranberry sauce.
Serves 6 adults, and is unsuitable for freezing.

Zucchini Pizza

1 x 12 inch or 30 cm ready-made pizza base

2–3 tablespoons pesto

50–75 g sun-dried tomatoes

approximately 1 ½ cups grated mozzarella cheese

1 zucchini, sliced

➤ Remove pizza base from wrapping and place on large baking tray. Spread pesto sauce evenly over base. Next, arrange the sun-dried tomatoes on top of pesto. Sprinkle mozzarella cheese to desired thickness over pesto and sun-dried tomatoes. Place zucchini evenly over the mozzarella and finish with another sprinkle of grated mozzarella cheese.

➤ Place pizza in a preheated 200°C oven and cook for 15 minutes or until cheese is golden brown and bubbling.

Serves 2 adults or 4 children, and can be frozen.

Sun-Dried Tomato Risotto

2 medium-sized zucchini

olive oil

45 g butter or dairy-free margarine

1 onion, chopped

1 cup arborio rice

1 chicken style Massel Ultracube

2 tomatoes, peeled and chopped (see page 65)

herb salt to taste

2 cloves garlic, crushed

50 g sun-dried tomatoes, chopped

100 g grilled or marinated capsicum, sliced (see note following recipe)

handful fresh basil, roughly chopped

► Wash and trim zucchini, and cut in half lengthwise. Lay out zucchini on baking tray and brush with olive oil. Place tray under grill on medium to high heat and allow zucchini to brown on both sides. Remove from heat, chop into pieces and set aside.

► In a large saucepan fry onion in melted butter on medium heat until onion is transparent. Add rice and stir until rice is coated with butter. Add 2 cups water, ultracube, tomatoes and herb salt. Allow mixture to simmer. The rice will start to absorb the liquid. Stir regularly.

► Once the rice has absorbed most of the liquid, add garlic, sun-dried tomatoes and capsicum. At this point you may need to add another ½ cup water. Continue to simmer, stirring regularly. When the rest of the liquid has been absorbed and rice is tender, add the basil and grilled zucchini. Remove risotto from heat and serve.

Serves 2–3 adults, and can be frozen.

NOTE: Sun-dried tomatoes and grilled or marinated capsicums can be bought at your local delicatessen. You can also purchase sun-dried capsicums, so if you would like to substitute this for grilled or marinated capsicums you can, but as it is lighter will need less than the recipe states.

If you want to grill your own capsicum, cut a red capsicum in half and de-seed it. Lay the two halves on a baking tray, shiny side up, and brush with olive oil. Place capsicum under the grill on medium to high heat and cook until skin is black and blistering. Remove from heat and allow to cool. Scrape the black capsicum skin away (washing under running water may help).

Pasta with Pesto

Pesto is an acquired taste but, once acquired, it's very addictive! This is for a child who's ready for the challenge of something different.

4 loosely packed cups fresh basil

3 cloves garlic

⅓ cup pine nuts

¼ cup grated Parmesan cheese

¼ cup olive oil

½ cup cream (optional)

➤ Place all ingredients except cream in a food processor or a tall jug or container, if using an upright Bamix type blender, and blend until ingredients are pureed. If mixture is a little dry, add a bit more olive oil. Add cream and blend until well combined. You can leave the cream out but the mixture will be very strong and you will need to use only a small amount per serving.

Cook up your child's or family's favourite pasta and top with a couple of spoons of pesto. For some colour, add some sliced sun-dried tomatoes.

Serves 4 adults. The pesto sauce freezes well on its own.

NOTE: this is a great dish to make if any of the family members have a cold. The combination of the garlic and basil seem to be a great pick-me-up.

Pumpkin Lasagna

olive oil

1 onion, chopped

2 kg pumpkin, peeled, seeded and chopped

large handful fresh chives, chopped

large handful fresh sage, chopped

sprinkle of nutmeg

sprinkle of herb salt

375 g fresh lasagna sheets

300 g fetta cheese

BECHAMEL SAUCE

50 g butter

2–3 tablespoons plain flour

500 ml milk or soy milk

➤ Fry onion in a little oil on medium heat in a saucepan until onion is transparent. Set aside.

➤ Steam pumpkin until soft, then mash well. Place pumpkin in a large bowl and add onion, herbs, nutmeg and herb salt, and stir until well combined. Set aside.

➤ Now make the bechamel sauce. Melt butter in a medium-sized saucepan, remove pan from heat and stir in flour. A whisk is helpful. You should now have a thick paste. Return pan to heat and add milk, whisking until the butter mixture and milk is well combined. Allow to thicken, stirring constantly, so mixture does not stick to the bottom of the pan. Once mixture has thickened remove pan from heat.

➤ To assemble lasagna, place a layer of lasagna sheets on the base of a baking dish.

➤ Place half the pumpkin mixture on top, spreading evenly. Crumble half the fetta over the top of the pumpkin and repeat process. Top with lasagna sheets, then pour bechamel sauce over the top. If you wish, you can sprinkle some grated cheese on top of the bechamel sauce.

➤ Place lasagna in a preheated 180°C oven and cook for approximately 35 minutes or until top is brown and bubbling.

Serves 6 adults, and can be frozen.
For children, try making lasagna in individual baking dishes.

NOTE: make sure pumpkin is cooked and mashed well, as lumps in lasagna are not desirable. A 28 x 32 cm baking dish was used for this recipe. If you have a smaller, deeper dish, you may be able to fit in 3 layers.

Chow Mein

oil

1 onion, chopped

2 stalks celery, sliced

¾ cup fresh green beans, sliced

1 chicken-style Massel Ultracube

½ x 125 g packet 'Realeat' vegie burger mix

½ teaspoon curry powder

soy sauce to taste

herb salt

½ Chinese cabbage, sliced

500–600 g fresh ready-to-eat noodles

➤ Fry onion in a little oil in a wok or large electric frypan on medium heat, until onion is soft. Add celery and beans, and cook for a few minutes. Add 2 cups hot water, ultracube, burger mix, curry powder, soy sauce and herb salt to taste. Mix well.

➤ Add cabbage and noodles and stir fry until cabbage has wilted and noodles are heated through.

Serves 4 adults, and is unsuitable for freezing.

NOTE: if fresh noodles are not available, use dried noodles of your choice. Allow approximately 85 g dried noodles per person.

Tofu and Chickpea Stir Fry

200 g smoked tofu, cut into medium-sized cubes

½ cup of oil for frying

variety of vegetables of choice sliced or chopped according to your
child's needs, for example:

4 button mushrooms

4 baby golden squash

2 stalks celery

2 zucchini

½ capsicum

3 spring onions

420 g tin Morroccan-style chickpeas

140 ml coconut milk or coconut cream

herb salt to taste

➤ In a wok or large electric frypan, fry tofu cubes in oil of choice,
until lightly browned. Remove tofu and drain on absorbent paper.
Pour off excess oil from wok and add chopped vegetables. Stir fry
vegetables until tender. Add chickpeas and coconut milk, and
combine with vegetables. Simmer for 5 minutes. Add salt to taste,
then add fried tofu.

Serve with rice of choice.
Serves 4 adults, and is unsuitable for freezing.

Tofu and Vegetables in Peanut Sauce

300 g firm tofu, cut into medium-sized cubes

oil

variety of vegetables of choice sliced or chopped to a manageable
size for your child, for example:

> 4–6 button mushrooms
>
> 2 zucchini
>
> 3–4 baby yellow squash
>
> 3 spring onions
>
> 1 small floret broccoli
>
> large handful snow peas

1 clove garlic, crushed

1 teaspoon grated ginger

juice of ½ a lemon

herb salt

PEANUT SAUCE

140 ml coconut milk or coconut cream

2 large tablespoons peanut butter

2–3 teaspoons brown sugar

➤ Heat some oil in a wok or large electric frypan on medium to high
heat and fry tofu until golden brown. Remove tofu, drain on
absorbent paper and set aside.

► Drain off excess oil from wok or frypan and stir fry vegies, adding broccoli and snow peas last. Add garlic, ginger, lemon juice and herb salt, and stir fry until vegies are tender. Reduce heat to the lowest setting and make the peanut sauce. Place coconut milk, peanut butter and brown sugar in a saucepan on medium heat. Combine well, allow to reach simmering point, then remove from heat. Add the peanut sauce to the vegetables, along with the fried tofu, and combine gently.

Serve with rice.
Serves 3 adults, and is unsuitable for freezing.

COOKING INSTRUCTIONS FOR LENTILS, RICE AND PASTA

Lentils — red and brown varieties

Red and brown lentils do not need to be pre-soaked. Remove the required amount of lentils from the packet and place in a colander or sieve and rinse well under the tap. Pick over the lentils to remove any foreign matter. When cooking, allow 3 cups of water to 1 cup of lentils. Place water and lentils in a saucepan and bring to boil on medium to high heat. Reduce the heat and allow to simmer for 20-30 minutes or until tender. Drain.

Leftover cooked lentils can be frozen up to 6 months.

NOTE: I have used canned beans and chickpeas throughout the recipes to save time for busy households. If you wish to use the dry beans and peas and prepare them yourself you need to soak them overnight or for 6–8 hours in a covered bowl in the fridge. The ratio to use for soaking is 2 cups of water to 1 cup of beans or peas. After soaking, drain and rinse well. When cooking, allow 3 cups of water to 1 cup of beans or peas. Place water and beans or peas in a saucepan and bring to boil on medium to high heat. Reduce the heat and allow to simmer until tender. Cooking time depends on the variety. Time could vary from 30 minutes to 90 minutes. You need to check on the back of packet for exact cooking time.

Rice — rapid boil method

Place rice and water in saucepan. Allow 1 cup of rice to approximately 6–8 cups of water. Bring to boil on high heat, and allow to boil until rice is tender. Drain.

NOTE: Cooking time will depend on variety of rice, short brown rice taking the longest (25–30 minutes), Jasmine or Basmati rice taking the least time to cook (12–15 minutes).

There are other methods in which to cook rice. If you wish to use these refer to instructions on back of packet.

Pasta

Pasta is rich in carbohydrates that are vital for energy which, for children, is important. The variety of pasta available is amazing. Pasta comes in so many shapes, sizes and colours, both dried and fresh, that it would be hard not to find something your children like. Pasta even comes in novelty shapes, which make mealtimes fun. The choice of what to put on your pasta is limitless. Supermarket shelves are packed with a mind-boggling array of pasta sauces. Experiment with both store-bought sauces and your own sauce recipes, and I'm sure you will come up with at least a few different pasta and sauce combinations that your child will love.

Allow water to boil in a medium to large saucepan on high heat. The size of your saucepan will depend on how much pasta you are cooking. You need to allow plenty of room for the pasta to move around in the saucepan while cooking. You can add 1–2 teaspoons of olive oil to the water to help prevent the pasta sticking. Once the water has boiled, add the pasta and allow to boil until pasta is tender. Drain.

NOTE: Cooking time will depend on whether it's dried or fresh and the type of pasta used. Check back of packet for instructions on cooking time.

REFERENCES

Brostoff, Dr Jonathon, and Gromlin, Linda, *The Complete Guide to Food Allergy Intolerance*, Bloomsbury, London 1989 (pp 8–9 and 196)

Child Accident Prevention Foundation of Australia

    A Safer Home for Children, May 1992

    A Parent's Guide to Kidsafe Homes, 1992

    Big Poisons for Little People

    Kidsafe. Child Safety in the Home

    Prevention of Choking on Food — Safe Eating for Children Under 4

CSIRO Australia — Division of Food Science and Technology

    Egg Quality and Storage, July 1992

    Handling Food in the Home, reprinted June 19

    Refrigerated Storage of Perishable Foods, April 1995

    The Safety of Microwave Ovens, March 1994

    Storage Life of Foods, reprinted June 1993

Lehmann, Chris (Editor), and Benham, Amanda, MDAA (Nutritional Editor), *Go Vegetarian! The Green Book on Vegetarian Nutrition*, The Australian Vegetarian Society, Paddington, NSW, 3rd edition, 1998

Messina, Virginia, MPH, RD, and Messina, Mark, PhD, *The Vegetarian Way: Total Health for You and Your Family*, Three Rivers Press, New York, 1996

Minchin, Maureen, *Food for Thought: A Parent's Guide to Food Intolerance*, Oxford University Press, 2nd edition, 1986 (pp 33 and 46)

Reader's Digest, *Foods that Harm, Foods that Heal: A–Z Guide to Safe and Healthy Eating*, 1997 (pp 282–285 and 358-359)

I would like to thank the following organisations for the information they provided to help me write this book:

- Dietetic Department of the Sydney Adventist Hospital, Sydney, Australia.

- Food Science Australia, Sydney, Australia.

- The Australian Nutrition Foundation, Sydney, Australia.

- Child Accident Prevention Foundation of Australia – Kidsafe, Sydney, Australia.

INDEX